MORAL TREATMENT

in American Psychiatry

MORAL
TREATMENT
in American
Psychiatry

By J. Sanbourne Bockoven, M.D.
*Superintendent, Cushing Hospital, Framingham,
Massachusetts;
Chairman, Committee on the History of Psychiatry,
American Psychiatric Association*

**SPRINGER PUBLISHING COMPANY, INC.
NEW YORK**

Reprinted with modifications and a new preface from the
Journal of Nervous and Mental Disease, Volume 124 (1956)
by permission of the Williams & Wilkins Company, Baltimore,
Maryland.

Library of Congress Catalog Card Number: 63-11841

Printed in USA

Preface

The substance of this book first appeared in the August and September issues of the *Journal of Nervous and Mental Disease* in 1956. At that time, moral treatment was not a topic in which psychiatrists had any particular interest. Indeed, were it not for the historical perspectives of Drs. Paul Yakovlev and Nolan D. C. Lewis, "Moral Treatment in American Psychiatry" would not have seen print.

In the course of the past seven years, however, there has been a rapid growth in the number of historical studies in psychiatry. Many papers and several books have been published. Even more striking is the reprinting of Pinel's "Treatise on Insanity," and Rush's "Observations on Diseases of the Mind," both of which were first published more than 150 years ago. The immediate reason for publishing "Moral Treatment" in book form was the demand for reprints which started about two years ago and has continued. Since the change in format meant resetting the type, a number of changes could be made in the text.

The book is the residue of gleanings from absorbing material on medical psychology and mental phenomena in general, as it was printed under the heading of "Moral Treatment" in the annual reports of our older hospitals and in early books and journals that are available in the libraries. This literature is significant, I believe, because it demonstrates that mental disorders could be understood and successfully treated, on the basis of many conceptual approaches, long before the modern era of scientific psychiatry. The success of moral treatment is, in some sense then, a humbling discovery, yet it is also a heartening one for it bids well for those who may become afflicted with mental ills in the future and for the mental health of all of us. This optimistic remark is based on the hopeful observation that the cultural climate of America today has already begun to encourage and support intensive study of mental phenomena and thorough cultivation of human individuality on a much vaster scale than that enjoyed by moral treatment in its beginnings. It seems most unlikely, furthermore, that our present mental health movement could possibly suffer the breakdown which brought that of our great-grandfathers to a halt.

This book would be a more satisfactory piece of scholarship if I had given more heed to the advice of my chiefs at Boston Psychopathic Hospital, Drs. Harry C. Solomon, Robert W. Hyde, and Milton Greenblatt. Yet without the disconcerting freedom, inspiration, and encouragement they gave me, the book would not exist at all. It would have considerable less content, too, but for Dr. Hyde's donation of scores of hours of enthusiastic knowledgeable discussion.

The reader will find that the tables and figures do not extend beyond 1950. He would naturally like to know what changes have occurred during the intervening years. Unfortunately, for this purpose, the methods of statistical reporting were changed in the first half of this period. The work involved in digging out the raw data is at this point prohibitive.

It will interest the reader to know, however, that the Worcester State Hospital, the subject of these tables and figures, has undergone considerable change during the period in question, especially since 1956. Under the direction of the Superintendent, Dr. Bardwell Flower, Worcester has, from my point of view, embarked once again on a program of moral treatment. The results are striking. The patient population has decreased from 2,693 patients in 1955 to 1,547 in 1962. This decrease in census has, furthermore, occurred in the face of a steadily rising rate of admission.

An adequate description of the treatment program which accomplished these results is beyond the scope of this preface.

Nevertheless, one feature bears reporting, namely, that supervised psychotherapy by nurses plays an important part. Once again, the physician at Worcester has a therapeutic team as he did in the days when moral treatment was given its first trial.

South Lincoln, Mass.   J. SANBOURNE BOCKOVEN, M.D.
October 17, 1962

Contents

I

Mental Hospitals: The Problem of Fulfilling Their Purpose

What is a mental hospital? Is it a permanent home for the insane and no different from what used to be called an insane asylum? Is it a place where people go for operations or medicines which cure certain kinds of illnesses? Or is it a place where people go to talk with psychiatrists about disturbing personal problems? There is today a growing volume of literature, both fiction and non-fiction, which seeks to elucidate the problems of individual failure and unhappiness by presenting them as understandable and solvable in terms of modern dynamic psychiatry. Science news reports, on the other hand, are keeping the citizen up to date on the development of wonder drugs or other medical and surgical treatments which cure mental disorders.

For the average citizen, there are many indications that medical science has already conquered or is very near conquering mental illness, but he also knows that from time to time the press has a great deal to say about bad conditions in mental hospitals. The massive collection of brick buildings, isolated from the rest of the community, several miles from town is still unknown to him. The sheer size and number of the buildings demonstrate that large numbers of people have to be kept locked up. This fact is difficult to reconcile with the indications that modern psychiatry knows how to cure mental illness. It serves

1

to intensify the feeling of dread which has always been associated with the word asylum.

The typical mental hospital as it exists in America today can be better understood if described and discussed in much the same terms that one would use in telling about a place such as a resort hotel, a naval vessel, a military post, or a university where he had lived for a period of time.

The typical mental hospital impresses a visitor approaching its grounds as having something of the appealing quality of a college campus, with the exception that there are almost no people passing to and fro on the walks. The administration building, in particular, differs little from that of a college. Its interior has an appearance of good taste and dignity, but again it is strangely quiet.

It is not until one enters the wards where the patients live that one feels the impact of what it means to be a patient in a typical mental hospital. Contrary to one's expectations, ward after ward may be passed through without witnessing the violent, the grotesque, or the ridiculous. Instead, one absorbs the heavy atmosphere of hundreds of people doing nothing and showing interest in nothing. Endless lines of people sit on benches along the walls. Some have their eyes closed; others gaze fixedly at the floor or the opposite wall. Occasionally, a head is turned to look out a window or to watch someone coming back from the toilet to take his place on a bench. All in all, it is a scene of inertness, listlessness, docility and hopelessness. Not so bad as might have been expected, one may think. Of course, there are worse wards where people lie on the floor naked and attendants are kept busy mopping up human excreta. Then there are intrepid patients who approach the visitor and plead for him to intercede in their behalf to help them get out of the hospital. And then again, someone may pace the floor who mutters to himself and thereby breaks the monotony. Or there may be a sudden chill of excitement when someone breaks into angry shouting for no apparent reason at all.

The visitor may well feel restless and irritated by the apathy of the patients and their willingness to waste these hours of their lives in meaningless tedium. His irritation may lead to his asking questions. If so, he learns that the attendant is proud of the ward because it is quiet and no mishaps have occurred while he was on duty; because the floor is clean; because the patients are prompt and orderly in going to and from meals. The visitor finds that the scene which appalls him with the emptiness and pointlessness of human life is regarded by the attendant as good behavior on the part of the patients. Thus introduced to the outlook of institutional psychiatry as it is practiced today, the visitor may well be puzzled, for there is little indication that it has anything to do with the psychiatry of current popular literature with its accent on hope and its accounts of enriching human life and showing the way to individual happiness. He must strain his imagination to see how the surrender of actually thousands of people to abject despair and inertia could possibly represent an improvement in their mental condition. On the contrary, he can envision himself going out of his mind if forced to spend many days in such a setting.

The more intimately acquainted a visitor becomes with the mental hospital, the sooner he reaches the final realization that it is engaged solely in the business of providing the physical needs and preserving the physical health and safety of rudderless, despairing people. He may come to admire the efficiency with which the basic operations of feeding, clothing, bathing, and laundering are performed. But he will wonder at the absence not only of treatment in the psychiatric sense but of any regimen whatsoever that the average layman would regard as conducive to mental health. He will learn that every patient is examined by a physician and given a psychiatric diagnosis. He will also learn that some newly admitted patients receive electric shock. But he cannot escape the overwhelming fact that patients numbered in the thousands receive no treatment for their mental disorders.

If the visitor talks with the physician and asks questions, he may be told that no treatment has yet been discovered which will cure the vast majority of the patients. Another physician trained in modern dynamic psychiatry may tell him that most of the patients could be treated with psychotherapy but that there are no psychotherapists available. Still another may tell him that one-third to one-half of the patients no longer need to be in the hospital because their illness has subsided. They remain in the hospital, he says, because there is no place for them to go and no one will give them a job. The superintendent will more than likely tell him that the hospital is crowded with more patients than it was built to care for, and that the hospital is badly understaffed and in need of many more attendants, nurses, social workers, and psychiatrists than the State budget provides or can be expected to provide. The visitor is then given to understand from the superintendent that the hospital as it is does not meet the needs of the patients, but the superintendent may also tell him that everything is being done for the patients that can be done in the way of cure of their mental illnesses.

The visitor can see for himself that the patients are dealt with by the hospital personnel on a mass basis and not as individuals. The patients are moved like an army from their sleeping quarters to their sitting places, to their eating places, and back to their sitting places. Movement occurs only in connection with getting out of bed, eating, and going back to bed.

There are some exceptions, for a number of patients do work in the various service centers of the hospitals such as the kitchen and the laundry. Others may work on the hospital farm or on the hospital grounds. There may be other patients who are allowed out of doors to take a walk in the fresh air. And there may be a select few patients who go to the occupational therapy department, where they are taught to make something with their hands. But even those patients, who do more than spend their days sitting, show by their expressionless faces and reluctance to speak that they have become accustomed to loneliness.

From observation of the great mass of patients, the visitor cannot help but be impressed with their obedience and conformity to the wishes of the hospital authorities. "But why," he may ask, "would the authorities wish the patients to lead an inactive, uncommunicative, lonely existence?" The answer he finds is that it is necessary to prevent the patients from exciting one another and creating a bedlam. The hospital authorities regard their chief objective to be protection of the patient from insane acts harmful to himself or others. All hospital personnel who come into contact with patients are taught to be constantly on the lookout for impending mishaps. They must also be on the alert to prevent the patients from getting hold of any article which might conceivably be used as a tool of destruction. Matches are not allowed, for a patient might set himself afire. Patients are not allowed to shave themselves lest they hide razor blades with which to cut their throats. Belts are not allowed lest patients hang themselves. Checker games are not allowed lest the patients attempt to swallow the checkers and choke. Every effort is made to prevent the recurrence of any dangerous act committed by any patient at any time in the past, and to anticipate any new way of committing one which might be invented in the future. (This might seem to rest on the theory that removal of all opportunity or occasion for insane acts or insane talk will eventually break the patient of insane habits and behavior.) The patients are handled as though their insanity were entirely due to an internal disorder and had nothing to do with the effects of external events on their emotions. Abuse of patients by personnel is strictly forbidden for obvious human reasons and not because it is thought that abuse has any effect on their illness.

There is total absence within the domain of the typical mental hospital of opportunity to participate in or give attention to any of the activities with which the members of any free community occupy themselves. Patients have neither the materials nor the freedom of movement to develop their talents or acquire skills, nor to have the experiences of ordinary life. They have nothing in their current lives to exchange with one another, either in the realm of material objects or of observations, that is not a tedious repetition of something already known to all. There is also total absence of application of any of the principles of mental hygiene in the day to day program of living in the hospital. There is no work; there is no play; there is no program of living.

The forced non-participation in human affairs of the mentally ill would necessarily seem to be based on certain knowledge that the mentally ill are wholly lacking in social intelligence, are totally incapable of perceiving the rights of others and are completely unable to learn to be members of society. The extreme caution exercised in the control of patients must be based on some such assumptions. These assumptions are, of course, in accord with the concept that mental illnesses are malignant, ineradicable diseases which totally destroy the capacity of the individual to behave like a human being or to be a person in any sense of the word.

One who visits the typical mental hospital will not find, however, that the hospital staff holds such a concept of mental illness. On the contrary, he will find that small-scale endeavors are made to provide the patients with entertainments and recreational opportunities which recognize their sensibilities as persons. He will learn that the extreme caution and the stringent restrictions placed on the vast majority of the patients are necessities resulting from the limited resources of the hospital in terms of personnel and facilities. The hospital has, in short, barely sufficient resources to discharge the minimal responsibility of preserving the patients from physical injury.

The visitor may detect a serious misunderstanding in the relation of the hospital to its source of financial support—the citizenry at large. The citizen assumes that the medical specialists who operate the public mental hospitals know that the wretched poverty of normal life activities in the hospital is an ineviitable consequence of the diseased mind. The medical director of the hospital, on the other hand, assumes that the citizenry is not interested in giving money or time to provide mentally ill patients with a fuller, busier, more worthwhile life. He regards the public disinterest as inevitable. The result of this impasse is that patients are seriously demoralized by the disrespect they suffer in being compelled to live subhuman lives. Indeed, it is difficult to find an example of members of lower species being compelled to suffer the indignity of functioning so far beneath their own level.

The foregoing account refers to many of the conditions of life in the hospital which prevent patients from taking part in practically all the activities engaged in by other people. Removal of these negative conditions constitutes a first and vitally important step toward raising the mental hospital to a level where it can perform the function for which it exists, namely, that of restoring the capacity of its patients to resume life outside the hospital.

The most damaging negative condition of the mental hospital is that which derives from what may fittingly be called the closed door policy. This policy not only locks patients in, but also locks out the mentally well members of society whose participation in hospital life can bring the interests and healthful breath of normality of the outside community into the hospital. The mingling of outsiders with patients does away with the deteriorating effects of monotony; it raises patients to their rightful status as human beings by demonstrating that they are recognized as worthy of being associates of citizens in good standing.

The mental hospital that welcomes outsiders within its walls and publicizes the need of its patients for normal human contacts has made an important step toward raising its standards of care. Outsiders who become volunteer workers soon recognize the multitudinous needs of patients and communicate them to the rest of the community. Sooner or later there will be a flow of goods into the hospital: books, magazines, playing cards, checkers, pictures, sewing materials, clothing, hot plates, coffee percolators, tea pots, radios, phonographs, and pianos. Besides material goods, outsiders will give time as instructors in such activities as dancing, sewing, and cooking.

As outsiders become better acquainted with the patients, they come to develop a personal interest in particular patients whom they may take on shopping trips and invite to their homes.

As a group, the volunteers may organize as a society which can raise funds for the benefit of patients.

The activities of volunteers greatly increases the traffic in and out of wards. This, in turn, leads to the discovery that locked doors are not only inconvenient but unnecessary. Patients who would ordinarily try to escape become more interested in the new activities than in running away. Along with the unlocking of doors comes a relaxation of other restrictions and rules which become not only too difficult to administer in a setting of activity, but also unnecessary. As patients regain contact with the community through their new friends, they not only learn of opportunities for jobs, but experience the advantage of being introduced to a prospective employer by a volunteer.

Adoption of an open-door policy is the first step toward raising the standards of care in a mental hospital. Equally important is the adoption of a policy of self-examination on the part of the administrative staff of the hospital in the interests of learning how its traditional functioning as a dictatorship impedes the effectiveness of the hospital personnel. Thought must be given to the advantages to be gained from democratic procedures which facilitate communication from below to above and, vice versa, make the knowledge and experience of those in top positions accessible to those dealing directly with patients. Freedom of expression and participation in policy determination by attendants stimulates their initiative and paves the way for the formation of patient organizations. The inclusion of patient organizations as responsible bodies having a role in the administrative affairs of the hospital is a powerful stimulus in motivating patients to acquire the social and political skills which are indispensable to successful living in the community.

The central theme of mental hospital improvement is removal of barriers to the development of all the positive assets of the mentally ill; there must be the maximum possible degree of freedom and access to whatever means help the patients become more useful citizens. The improvement of the mental hospital requires what is essentially a social revolution in the management of the mentally ill. It involves casting off the antiquated asylum methods which were dictated by ignorance and prejudices of the past and are perpetuated by fear and misunderstanding.

Recent developments in the treatment of the mentally ill which impose minimal obstructions to the patient's participation in society are the establishment of clinics for the treatment of psychoses on an out-patient basis, the establishment of psychiatric wards in general hospitals, and the increase in the number of psychiatrists in private practice who treat patients in their offices.

In the following chapters we will give an account of what human endeavor in America has done, and can be expected to do, toward relief of the severe grades of mental illness which require individuals to be in mental hospitals. There are three phases in American psychiatry. The first phase is one of understanding care which our society sought to give the mentally ill when democracy was young and inspired with its mission to mankind. The second phase is one of decline in human understanding which accompanied social changes during the course of the nineteenth century. The third phase is that of the new hope which modern understanding of human thought, feeling, and behavior has for victims of nervous breakdowns.

The American people are faced with the responsibility of learning what psychiatry today has to offer the mentally ill and how to bring its benefits to them. Americans are not as yet fully aware of the most significant aspect of modern scientific knowledge of the hospitalized mentally ill—namely their great need *for psychological aid and moral support which all people in distress need and which our society is able to give if it is motivated to do so*. Scientific controversy within psychiatry over the validity of particular psychological theories and techniques still obscures from public view the great importance of bringing ordinary psychological and material aids to the mentally ill who are deprived of all contacts in our mental hospitals as they are now constituted.

The condition of the institutionalized mentally ill in America today is largely the result of public opinion led astray. The harmful public attitude, formed under the influence of "scientific" authority which pronounced mental illness incurable over three-quarters of a century ago, contradicts the primary value of the individual and harms many people. And it is the people, primarily, who can do something about the enormous number of man-years of wasted living which attends present-day institutional management of the mentally ill.

II

Moral Treatment—
Forgotten Success in the
History of Psychiatry

Backsliding has time and again followed progress in man's understanding of self and neighbor. Periods of enlightenment at times left an imprint strong enough to survive generations of darkness and inspire progress anew. At other times, the principles on which these periods were based had to be rediscovered. On the whole, progress over the centuries has been substantial. Religion, politics, and science have all made their contributions.

The greatest challenge to the capacity of men (individually and collectively) to understand neighbor and self arises when mental illness disrupts their relationship to one another. Society's reaction to the mentally ill has oscillated throughout recorded history between brutality and benevolence. When neither was extreme, neglect was the rule.

A basis for understanding human behavior was laid by Plato, who wrote: "And indeed it may almost be asserted that all intemperance in any kind of pleasure, *and all disgraceful conduct*, is not properly blamed as the consequence of voluntary guilt. For no one is voluntarily bad; but he who is depraved becomes so through a certain habit of body, and an ill-governed education. All the vicious are vicious through two most involuntary causes, which we shall always ascribe to the planters, than to the things planted, and to the trainers than to those trained." (6)

Hippocrates declared the behavior in psychoses to be due to brain disease and decried belief in demon possession.

These elements of understanding were lost to mankind for several hundred years, to reappear in the writings of Coelius Aurelianus and again disappear during the Dark Ages. They were once more brought to light by Paracelsus and John Weyer. These sixteenth century physicians raised their voices against abuses arising from superstition and warped theological interpretation of the symptoms of mental illness. Their influence led to partial acceptance of mental disorder as a province of medicine.

Consistent care and scientific clinical study were not adopted until the eighteenth century when liberal philosophy and political movements contained the hope that science would enable the achievement of humanitarian ends. The possibility that science could solve the riddle of mental illness captured the imagination. In this endeavor, the goals of science and humanitarianism were undistinguishable. There was no clear-cut line indicating where elimination of abuse ended and scientific therapy began.

The method of the humanistic science of the eighteenth century involved clearing the mind of *a priori* bias in order that it might uncover universal laws. The assumption that laws of science as yet undiscovered were universal (in the sense that the "law" of falling bodies was universal) carried with it the connotation that human behavior, too, was the result of laws. Hence, human behavior must be influenced greatly by unknown forces over which the individual could not have complete control. This had the effect of emphasizing those qualities which individuals have in common and the impossibility of an absolute standard of individual responsibility. Logically, then, all men could be looked upon as equal, and their evil actions could be forgiven. Democratic government and humanitarian treatment of criminals, paupers, and psychotics thus appeared to have their foundations in science.

Humanitarianism favored the view that lunatics had undergone stresses which robbed them of their reason. That such stress could result from disappointment as well as inflammation was a basic assumption. Stresses of a psychological nature were referred to as *moral causes*. Treatment was called *moral treatment*, which meant that the patient was made comfortable, his interest aroused, his friendship invited, and discussion of his troubles encouraged. His time was managed and filled with purposeful activity.

The use of the word "moral" in the terms *moral causes* and *moral treatment* has, at first glance, the capacity to arouse animosity in modern man acquainted with that literature of anthropology and social psychology which demonstrates the relativity of moral standards. Knowledge that the early psychiatrist used "moral" as the equivalent of "emotional" or "psychological" serves to allay such animosity. Reflection on the genesis and meaning of the word "moral" discloses the logic of the usage. The term is intimately related to the word "morale" and carries within it emotional connotations of such words as zeal, hope, spirit, and confidence. It also has to do with custom, conduct, way of life, and inner meaning. "Moral" (and "ethics," too) has many shades of meaning with respect to interpersonal relations, besides having to do with abstract ideas, right and wrong and good and evil.

The word "moral" in *moral treatment* and *moral causes* bears within it an implication, too, about moral responsibility, namely, that the mentally ill were not morally responsible for their acts which were assumed to result either from ignorance or incorrect understanding. Indeed, to its founders, moral treatment of the mentally ill was considered to be a moral mandate on those who were more fortunate. Moral treatment was never clearly defined, possibly because its meaning was self-evident during the era in which it was used. It meant compassionate and understanding treatment of innocent sufferers. Even innocence was not a prerequisite to meriting compassion. Compassion was extended to those whose mental illness was thought due to willful and excessive indulgence in the passions.

Moral treatment is of great significance in the history of psychiatry. It was the first practical effort made to provide systematic and responsible care for an appreciable number of the mentally ill, and it was eminently successful in achieving recoveries.

The great step to moral treatment was taken almost simultaneously by a French physician and an English Quaker in the last decade of the eighteenth century. Phillipe Pinel transformed a madhouse into a hospital, and William Tuke built a *retreat* for the mentally ill. Similar reforms were wrought in Italy, Germany, and America by Chiarugi, Reil, and Rush. Pinel has priority on the debt the world owes for moral treatment. The reforms of Benjamin Rush in America, though not as extensive as those of Pinel, were based on inspiration derived from the same source. Both were steeped in the liberal writings of the physician-philosopher John Locke. Rush did much to stimulate the interest of American physicians in mental illness and paved the way for full acceptance of the principles of moral treatment.

Although the mentally ill had for many years been accepted as patients in several hospitals in America (namely, the Pennsylvania Hospital, the New York Hospital, the Eastern State Hospital at Williamsburg, Virginia, and the Maryland Hospital at Baltimore), it was not until 1817, four years after Rush's death, that a hospital was founded in America expressly for the purpose of providing moral treatment. This hospital, patterned after the York Retreat in England, was built by Pennsylvania Quakers and named the Friends' Asylum. Within seven years, three more privately endowed mental hospitals were built: McLean, Bloomingdale, and the Hartford Retreat. Within thirty years, eighteen hospitals had been built for moral treatment of the mentally ill in America.

The high standards of hospitals built by private philanthropy set a good example for the many state-supported institutions which soon came into being. First of these was the Eastern State Hospital at Lexington, Kentucky, built in 1824, the same year as the Hartford Retreat in Connecticut. Within the next ten years, four more state hospitals were built, now known as the Manhattan State Hospital (New York), 1825; the Western State

Hospital (Staunton, Virginia), 1828; the South Carolina State Hospital (Columbia), 1828; and the Worcester State Hospital (Massachusetts), 1833.

The Worcester State Hospital merits special attention because of the role it played in the history of moral treatment. The first superintendent at Worcester was Dr. Samuel B. Woodward, who, with Dr. Eli Todd, had persuaded the Connecticut Medical Society to sponsor the founding of the Hartford Retreat. The two physicians were long-standing friends who, in their practice of general medicine, shared an abiding interest in the treatment of mental disorders. Both became "specialists" of their day; patients with mental diseases were referred to them by other physicians.

These pioneer psychiatrists conducted a survey of mental illness in Connecticut to determine the size of hospital necessary to care for the mentally ill of that state. The elder of the two, Dr. Todd, was appointed superintendent of the Retreat. Nine years later, Dr. Woodward was chosen superintendent of the hospital at Worcester, the first state institution for the mentally ill in New England. This hospital was built largely through the enthusiastic support of Horace Mann, father of the American public school. It might be mentioned in passing that the New Hampshire State Hospital was founded largely through the efforts of Dr. Luther Bell (who later became superintendent of McLean Hospital) and the clergymen of New Hampshire. These are but a few examples of the active support which professional men—clergymen, educators, physicians—gave in behalf of the mentally ill in the early history of American psychiatry.

Worcester State Hospital under the direction of Dr. Woodward served as a proving ground for moral treatment and demonstrated beyond doubt that recovery was the rule. Year after year Dr. Woodward gave the statistics of recovery in the Annual Reports of his hospital.

It was Dr. Todd, however, who first called the attention of the public to the success of moral treatment. He reported recovery in over 90% of patients who had been admitted to the Hartford Retreat with mental illness of less duration than one year. This result was based on relatively few admissions, however, and it remained for Dr. Woodward to demonstrate, on the basis of a large series of cases, that recovery was the rule in recently ill patients.

It is pertinent at this point to present the statistics kept by the Worcester State Hospital during the time moral treatment was still applicable, that is, before crowding and expansion beyond optimum size fully disrupted vital interpersonal relationships among patients, attendants, and physicians.

Table 1 shows the number and per cent discharged as recovered or improved of the total number of patients admitted who had been ill less than one year prior to their admission. During

TABLE 1—OUTCOME IN PATIENTS ADMITTED TO
WORCESTER STATE HOSPITAL WHO WERE ILL LESS THAN
ONE YEAR PRIOR TO ADMISSION, 1833-1852

(*Data from the Annual Reports of the Hospital*)

Five-Year Period	Patients Admitted	Patients Discharged	
		Recovered	Improved
1833–37	300	211 (70 %)	39 (8.3%)
1838–42	434	324 (74.6%)	14 (3.2%)
1843–47	742	474 (63.9%)	34 (4.6%)
1848–52	791	485 (61.3%)	37 (4.7%)

twenty years there were 2,267 such admissions, of whom 1,618 were discharged as recovered or improved, or 71% (66% recovered, 5% improved). During this same period the total of all admissions (including those whose illness had lasted longer than one year prior to admission) was 4,119, of whom 2,439 or 59% were discharged as recovered (45%) or improved (14%).

Such statistical data invite attention to the assumptions on which the idea of moral treatment was based and its cultural setting. America in the 1830's and '40's was rapidly developing a new liberal philosophy of the individual. Leading American thinkers of the period turned to nature in search of truth. Societies were formed for the abolition of slavery. Experiments were made in communal living. A spirit of freedom and self-expression was in the air. New England Puritanism was growing milder. The jealous God of Cotton Mather was becoming the loving God of William Channing, and a new intellectual independence was coming to the fore. Emerson encouraged the individual to self-reliance, and in one of his addresses, "The Scholar," he stated, "The world is nothing, the man is all." Historically, in the United States, this period has been referred to by Fisher as "The Rise of the Common Man, 1820–1850."

American thought was at this time in close communion with the romantic movement in Germany. American psychiatry was influenced by the then current psychobiological trend in German psychiatric literature. In particular, the long forgotten von Feuchtersleben was often referred to by American psychiatrists. Dr. Gregory Zilboorg has credited von Feuchtersleben's view of mental illness in the 1840's as being much the same as that of present-day psychiatry.

One of the leading spokesmen of early American psychiatry was Dr. Isaac Ray, whose psychiatric career began in the 1830's as superintendent of the Augusta State (Maine) Hospital. Dr. Ray subscribed to the view that the mind includes those qualities which make possible the relations among people which have to do with man's greatest welfare. Love and hate were to him as much manifestations of mind as rational processes. He also contended that every appetite and faculty must have its means of gratification and protested that belief to the contrary was wholly repugnant. He believed in the unity of the individual man and referred specifically to the unity of mind and brain. In his book "Mental Hygiene" (1863) he gave particular attention to the influence of passions, emotions, and temperament on mental health. He strongly recommended, after von Feuchtersleben, that ill-humored individuals be regarded as suffering from disease and advised them to seek every means to rid themselves of it to prevent becoming insane. He also held the view that insanity is but an exaggeration of personality traits which in their less extreme form are regarded as merely disagreeable.

Both Dr. Ray and his colleague, Dr. John S. Butler, superintendent of the Hartford Retreat, were impressed with the importance of child rearing to mental health. Dr. Butler categorically stated that he had traced the cause of insanity to the malign influences in childhood in a large proportion of over 3,000 patients he had personally studied. Dr. Butler also voiced a commonly held opinion of the times that all bodily processes are under the influence of the mind.

The psychodynamic and psychosomatic orientation of psychiatry in the early 1800's found its fullest expression in the elaboration of the psychological therapeutic approach known as the moral treatment of insanity. In the language of Dr. Ray, the proper administration of moral treatment required that the physician learn through inquiry and conversation what occupies the minds of his patients. It required further that he investigate the mental make-up of patients' relatives. The greatest requirement of all was that the physician spare no effort in gaining the confidence and good will of his patients and strive to discover their experiences and supply their needs. The recommendation was made that the physician acquire a large fund of knowledge in order to converse with patients on matters interesting to them and thus gain an understanding of their inner life. The physician was strongly reminded that even the most insane patients are sensitive to manifestations of interest and good will. He was warned, however, to limit the number of patients in his care to those he can know personally.

Although much emphasis was placed on the relationship between physician and patient, moral treatment embraced a much larger psychological approach than individual psychotherapy. Indeed, perhaps the greatest asset of moral treatment was the attention it gave to the value of physical setting and social influences of hospital life as curative agents. In his book "Curability of Insanity" (7), published in 1887, Dr. Butler repeatedly points out the importance of scrutinizing the hospital environment to find and remove whatever is depressing or disturbing. He insists that a cheerful, sympathetic atmosphere and esthetic appeal are essential for the cure of many patients. His goal was to make hospital wards as homelike as possible, for he placed great faith in the value of family-like gatherings in which patients could discuss their problems among themselves and with the physician. He also believed that confidential interviews with patients were essential, but he was convinced that the turning point in many a patient's illness took place in group discussions. He also insisted that appropriate social influences could not be maintained if hospitals were allowed to care for more than 200 patients at one time. He considered monotony to be the greatest obstacle to be overcome in mental hospitals and believed heartily in promoting a wide variety of activities for patients.

The theoretical foundation of early American psychiatry and the success of its therapeutic approach to insane individuals as persons were a source of inspiration to those who believed in the dignity of man and sought to improve his condition. Charles Dickens and Horace Mann were particularly impressed by the experience of seeing moral treatment in action. In his 1833 report (16), as chairman of the board of trustees of the Worcester State Hospital, Horace Mann told a moving story of 32 fellow beings who had been restored to their reason under the influences of the hospital, whose loss to their families would otherwise have been mourned without hope. He told further of the unbelievable changes which had taken place in those patients who had not recovered. When the hospital was first opened, there were at least one hundred patients who would assail any human being who came near them. In less than a year only 12 of these patients were still assaultive. Similarly, of 40 patients who would tear off their clothing in the beginning, only 8 still did so at the time of the report. He commented on the civility and kindness which had come to prevail among the patients. Wailing, raving, and desponding were dispelled, and the facial expression of patients reflected their improved state of mind. He credited these heartening results to the efforts "of all those engaged in administering the daily affairs of the institution to exclude, as far as in any manner possible, all causes of mental disquietude, by substituting persuasion by force, by practicing forebearance, mildness, and all the nameless offices of humanity, by imbuing, in every practicable way, the minds of the patients with a new set of pleasing, cheerful, grateful and benevolent emotions." He summed up the idea of moral treatment in the following words: "The whole scheme of moral treatment is embraced in a single idea—humanity—the law of love—that sympathy which appropriates another's consciousness of pain and makes it a personal relief from suffering whenever another's sufferings are relieved."

Charles Dickens' account (9) of his visit to the Boston State Hospital in 1842 brings to light still more facets of hospital life in the moral treatment era. He commented on the wide variety of activities available to patients, including carriage rides in the open air, fishing, gardening, and several kinds of indoor and outdoor games. Patients worked with sharp-edged tools and ate their meals with knives and forks. The patients organized themselves in a sewing circle which held meetings and passed resolutions. They also attended dances which were held weekly. Dickens was particularly surprised with the self-respect which was inculcated and encouraged in the patients by the superintendent's attitude toward them. He made special note that the superintendent and his family dined with the patients and mixed among them as a matter of course.

The psychological orientation of moral treatment and the recoveries from psychosis accompanying its application cannot be lightly dismissed. Modern psychiatry would do well to regard the mental hospitals of the early nineteenth century as pilot hospitals which demonstrated the value of social and psychological factors in treatment. The reason this finding was largely disregarded for nearly one hundred years is a story in itself. The least we can do is borrow a leaf from our psychiatric forefathers and give full attention to the possibilities of treating psychoses by social and psychological means in the many state and federal hospitals which have so long considered psychosis curable *only* by physical or chemical means.

III

The Breakdown of
Moral Treatment

It is of great importance to the understanding of forces with which modern psychiatry must contend to determine why moral treatment did not become an enduring basic principle of psychiatric care rather than a soon forgotten temporary success. A successful technique in whatever field of endeavor is not ordinarily abandoned unless displaced by a still more effective technique. Moral treatment, however, simply passed out of existence. It was followed by the void of custodial care.

Of the many factors which contributed to the decline and the eventual discard of moral treatment, lack of inspired leadership after the death of its innovators was probably the most important. The founders of moral treatment were shortsighted in not providing for their own successors in numbers adequate to meet the needs of the future. These leaders each trained but one or two physicians, not enough to replace themselves and staff their own growing hospitals, let alone the numerous hospitals soon to be built. By the time of the Civil War, moral treatment was already crippled by the deaths of the leading moral therapists. Dr. Eli Todd died in 1833; Dr. Woodward resigned from the Worcester State Hospital in 1845 and died in 1850. Dr. Amariah Brigham, editor of the Americian Journal of Insanity, superintendent of the Utica State Hospital and one of the most vigorous writers on the subject of moral treatment, died in 1849. In the same year, Dr. Pliny Earle resigned from Bloomingdale (see Chapter

IV) and did not reenter the field of moral treatment until 15 years later. Dr. Stedman resigned from the Boston State Hospital in 1851. Dr. Luther Bell resigned his position as superintendent of McLean Hospital in 1856. Machinations in Ohio State politics forced Dr. William Awl to resign as superintendent of the Ohio State Hospital in 1850. Dr. John Galt died in 1862, and Nehemiah Cutler in 1859. In 1867, Dr. Isaac Ray resigned from the Butler Hospital, and five years later Dr. Butler resigned from the Hartford Retreat. In 1874, Dr. Stribling died.

Only four of the original 13 fathers of American psychiatry and founders of moral treatment survived the 1870's, and two of these had retired to private practice: Dr. Isaac Ray and Dr. John S. Butler. Dr. Pliny Earle continued as superintendent of the Northampton (Mass.) State Hospital until 1885, and Dr. Thomas Kirkbridge of the Pennsylvania Hospital until 1883. The former, although an avid proponent of moral treatment, was paradoxically one of the strongest forces in discrediting its results. Unfortunate events in his life in conjunction with a tendency to despondency and pessimism help explain the stand he took. These circumstances will be discussed in connection with statistical studies of treatment results in Chapter IV.

Lack of foresight in training sufficient numbers of moral therapists for the future was matched by failure to plan ahead for the building of a sufficient number of hospitals. It is presumptuous, of course, to imply that such planning should be expected. No one could have had an inkling of the impending rapid growth in population of the eastern seaboard and the accompanying shift from a rural to an urban mode of life which took place during the second half of the nineteenth century. It was not until 1874 that any particular mention was made of the great increase in the number of patients in the mental hospitals of Massachusetts. In the annual report of the State Board of Health of that year, Dr. Edward P. Jarvis, psychiatrist and recognized statistician, pointed out that all the state's mental hospitals had been enlarged to accommodate far more patients than the original plans allowed. Thirteen years later, Dr. John S. Butler (in his book "Curability of Insanity") sought to influence the

American Psychiatric Association to place a limit on the size of mental hospitals. He invoked the resolutions passed by that association in 1844 and 1851 which stated that the preferable maximum size for a mental hospital was two hundred patients. He decried the resolution passed in 1866 which allowed hospitals to have a capacity for six hundred patients and pointed out that it in effect placed no limit since hospitals had already expanded beyond that number. He quoted Drs. Isaac Ray and Thomas Kirkbridge and other surviving pioneers of moral treatment to the effect that large hospitals harmed patients by denying them personal attention and caused them to be treated like a mob in which they lost their human attributes.

Needless to say, Dr. Butler and his colleagues were not heeded. State hospitals reached an average of 1,000 patients many decades ago and now exceed 2,000, with no limit in sight. The Worcester State Hospital is an example of the steady increase in resident population especially since the time of the Civil War (Fig. 1). Recurrent cycles of overcrowding were met by depriving patients of recreational space. With each new construction for sleeping quarters, there was a further relative decrease in the space and means for recreation, which in turn demanded an increase in regimentation of patients. The rapid increase in hospital population included another factor of great importance, that of the immigration beginning in the post-Civil War period. The influx of patients from poverty-stricken immigrant families into the mental hospital put a severe strain on the flexibility and breadth of understanding of the medical officers of the hospitals. Psychiatrists of old American stock who were filled with compassion on beholding mental illness in one of their own were filled with revulsion by what they considered uncouth and ignorant in the insane foreign pauper. As the proportion of immigrant patients in the hospital increased, there was a tendency for hospital living quarters to deteriorate until they were nothing more than barren dormitories adjoining even more barren day-rooms whose furniture consisted of crude benches along the walls. The resulting apathy of the patients led their physicians to express the belief that they were in no way

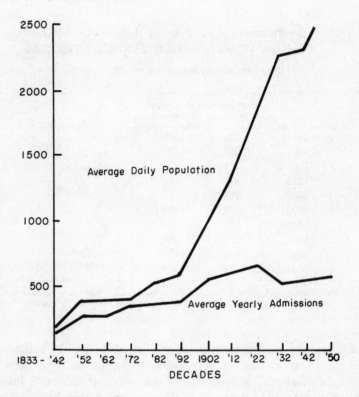

Fig. 1. Resident population and yearly admission rates of Worcester State Hospital, 1833-1950. (*Data from the Annual Reports of the Hospital*)

capable of appreciating anything better. This example of rationalized callousness provides some idea of the degrading effect which compromise can produce when the dignity of the individual is forgotten.

Passages from the Annual Reports of the Worcester State Hospital leave little doubt that racial prejudice played a role in the breakdown not only of moral treatment but of ordinary decent hospital living standards. Mention of foreigners as a problem was first made in the Annual Report of 1854, which laments that the State Hospital was fast becoming a hospital for Irish immigrants rather than for the intelligent Yeomanry of Massachusetts who could pay their board and would not ask

TABLE 2.—PROPORTION OF FOREIGN-BORN AMONG PATIENTS
ADMITTED TO WORCESTER STATE HOSPITAL, 1844-1933

(*Data from the Annual Reports of the Hospital*)

Year	Number of Admissions	Proportion of Foreign-Born	
1844	236	10%	
1854	288	38%	Percentages
1863	215	47%	based on
1873	470	38%	total
1883	275	?	admissions
1893	534	67%	
1903	553	45%	Percentages
1913	515	46%	based on
1923	402	53%	first
1933	484	45%	admissions

Note: These particular foreign-born were usually destitute. Mental hospitals were becoming *vast almshouses*—just as today they are becoming "old folks homes."

for charity. A plea was made for the "classification" of patients, by which was meant the segregation of foreigners from native New Englanders. The basis for the plea was that the sensibilities of patients reared in the proverbially neat and orderly households of New England were offended by close contact with those who were accustomed to and satisfied with filthy habitations and filthier habits.

Yankee physicians found it difficult to identify with the Irish immigrant. Moral treatment and the "law of love" extolled by Horace Mann were reserved for those of Yankee stock. Indeed, in the Annual Report of 1858 (Worcester State Hospital) the Irish were castigated for a variety of reasons, among which were: receiving high wages in prosperous times, gratifying vicious indulgences, seeking labor in the most menial capacity, huddling together in the most objectionable places, neglecting all the rules of health, and preferring the solace of rum and tobacco to the quiet, intelligent influences of well-ordered homes.

"Foreign insane pauperism" was the name given to the problem of mental illness in the immigrant population. Its disrupting effects were due not only to racial and religious incompatibilities, but also to economic factors. Patients without settlement in Massachusetts were paid for by the Commonwealth. All other patients' bills were paid either by their families or by the towns in which they resided. The Commonwealth paid so little for its pauper patients that the hospital was forced to charge the towns and families more. In the Annual Report of the State Board of Health of 1874, Dr. Edward Jarvis pointed out that proportionately few of the mentally ill patients of self-sustaining families were sent to state hospitals; most of them were kept at home because they could not pay and were ashamed to "go on the town," whereas the poverty stricken did not hesitate to use the hospitals. Rapid population growth, immigration, and pauperism forced the metamorphosis of mental hospitals from home-like havens of moral treatment to huge custodial asylums. Table 2 shows the proportion of foreign-born in each of the years indicated. If patients of foreign-born parents had been included, the proportion of what the trustees and superintendent of Worcester called foreigners would be much greater in the latter decades of the century.

The phenomenon of the mentally ill from destitute families crowding out and, in effect, preventing the hospitalization of mentally ill from self-sustaining families led to further deterioration of mental hospitals. The attitude that paupers would not appreciate nice things anyway provided a rationalization for not insisting on higher standards. On the other hand, many home recoveries must have occurred among the mentally ill of self-sustaining families who could not afford hospital care. These were probably treated by private practitioners such as Edward P. Jarvis, William Hammond, and Silas Weir Mitchell.

The deterioration in mental hospital living standards through the latter part of the nineteenth century is shown graphically in Fig. 2. For example, in 1869 the weekly per capita income of the United States was $4.00. The weekly cost per patient at Worcester State Hospital was also $4.00. In 1899, the weekly

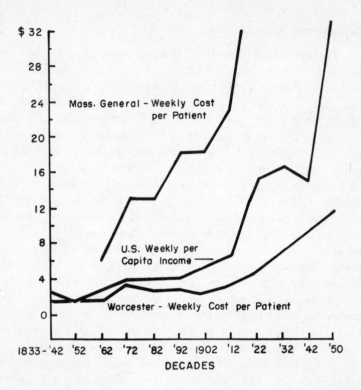

FIG. 2. Worcester State Hospital per capita weekly cost, and Massachusetts General Hospital per capita weekly cost, compared with United States per capita weekly income, 1833-1950. (*Adapted from "The Hospital in Contemporary Life" (Edited by Nathaniel W. Faxon, M.D., Harvard University Press, Cambridge, 1949) and the Annual Reports of the Worcester State Hospital, 1833-1940*)

per capita income of the United States had gone up to $5.00, and the weekly cost per patient at Worcester had *dropped* to $3.50. The Massachusetts General Hospital weekly cost per patient in 1869 was $10.00 and in 1899 was $14.00. Weekly per capita income of the United States by 1929 had gone up to $13.00, or more than tripled since 1869. Massachusetts General's weekly cost per patient had *quadrupled,* while Worcester's had not even *doubled* (from $4.00 to just under $7.00). The general hospital ran ahead of per capita income, while the mental hospital ran behind. To the public, the former was expensive and the latter cheap. Thus mental illness was given, in addition to the universal stigmas, a further one, "cheap," with the peculiar connotation it has in America.

Any criteria adopted for comparing standards of hospital care provided in different eras are fraught with error. Data with respect to the Worcester State Hospital allow construction of indices which may to a certain extent reflect changes in the standards of care during the last century.

The ratio of the number of resident patients per physician for each decade over a period of 100 years is an index of this change. Table 3 shows how the ratio increased over the entire period. The table also shows the ratio of the number of patients per each attendant over the same period. Here a trend in the opposite direction is shown. From decade to decade each attendant had fewer patients in his charge.

In 1904, the 70-hour work week was adopted. From that time on some of the attendants worked night shifts; thus the ratio of patients per attendant at any given time may have been less than indicated in Table 3 after that date. Prior to 1904, the attendants usually had quarters in the wards and were always with the patients, except for a few hours each Saturday.

The relative decrease in the number of physicians and the relative increase in the number of attendants resulted in a large increase in the ratio of the number of attendants to each physician over the 110 years. In the decade 1913-22, the number of attendants to each physician was three times as great as in the decade 1833-42, and 1843-52.

The scale of pay for physicians during the 1890's was more than double that of the 1830's and '40's (from $500 to $1,000 per year for assistant physicians and from $1,200 to $3,000 per year for superintendents), while the scale for attendants only increased about 50% (from $15 a month to $23-$25 a month).

During the 1830's, there were, on the average, two doctors and 15 attendants at the Worcester State Hospital. During the 1930's, there were, on the average, 14 doctors and 336 attendants. The standards of care given the patients in terms of personal relationships suffered in proportion to the increase in social

TABLE 3.—PATIENT-PHYSICIAN-ATTENDANT RATIOS
AT WORCESTER STATE HOSPITAL, 1833-1950

(*Data from the Annual Reports of the Hospital*)

Years	Resident Patients		Attendants
	Per Physician	Per Attendant	Per Physician
1833–1842	88	12	8
1843–1952	127	15	8
1853–1862	128	—	—
1863–1872	156	—	—
1873–1882	146	—	—
1883–1892	132	8	13
1893–1902	114	11	11
1903–1912	148	10	15
1913–1922	205	9	24
1923–1932	175	9	20
1933–1942	165	7	24
1943–1950	230	11	21

distance between physicians and attendants. Opportunities for physicians and attendants to discuss problems of individual patients became fewer.

The retardation of research in mental hospitals and the deterioration of care given patients did not long continue unnoticed. By 1875, members of the rising specialty of neurology had formed their own society—a society which in its early years not only specifically excluded from membership physicians in the employ of mental hospitals, but openly challenged their authority to speak on matters of mental illness. In 1879, the first direct attack on mental hospitals and their medical officers was made by William A. Hammond in a paper, "The Non-Asylum Treatment of the Insane." The first two paragraphs indicate its tenor:

"It is the commonly received opinion among physicians and the public generally that as soon as possible after an individual becomes insane, he or she must be placed under the restraint of a lunatic asylum. No matter what the type of mental aberration, no matter what the facilities for receiving care and attention at home, the asylum is regarded as the necessary destination of the one so unfortunate as to be deprived wholly, or in part, of the light of reason. For this state of affairs, the medical officers of insane asylums are mainly responsible, for they have very diligently inculcated the idea that they alone, by education, by experience and by general aptitude, are qualified to take the medical superintendence of the unfortunate class of patients in question, and that restraint and separation from friends and acquaintances are measures in themselves which are specially curative in their influence.

"It will be among the chief objects of this memoir to show that these views are erroneous; that the medical profession (outside the hospital) is, as a body, fully as capable of treating cases of insanity as cases of any other disease, and that in many instances sequestration is not only unnecessary but positively injurious." (21)

In 1894, Dr. Weir Mitchell administered a verbal spanking to the members of the medico-psychological society on its fiftieth anniversary:

"The cloistered lives you lead give rise, we think, to certain mental peculiarities. I could tell you how to mend them. I shall by and by. You hold to and teach certain opinions which we have long learned to lose. One is the superstition (almost is it that) to the effect that an asylum is in itself curative. You hear the regret in every report that patients are not sent soon enough, as if you had ways of curing which we have not. Upon my word, I think asylum life is deadly to the insane. Poverty, risk, fear, send you many patients; many more are sent by people quite able to have their friends treated outside. They are placed in asylums because of the wide-spread belief you have so long, as we think, so unreasonably fostered, to the effect that there is some mysterious therapeutic influence to be found behind your walls and locked doors. We hold the reverse opinion, and think your hospitals are never to be used save as a last resort." (24)

Tucker's report on "Lunacy in Many Lands," based on an

extensive inspection tour of mental hospitals of the world, was published in 1887. Unbelievably bad hospital conditions were practically universal. It is a sad comment on the state of psychiatry that Tucker's chief plea was merely for decent standards of living for the mentally ill and elimination of mechanical restraint and enforced baths. Probably the most severe castigation of psychiatry was that by Franklin B. Sanborn, who, as chairman of the Board of State Charities (Massachusetts) for 35 years, had become well acquainted with the medical officers of mental hospitals. In a pamphlet published in 1899, bearing the title "A Remonstrance in the Name of the Insane Poor Against Crowding Them into Hospital Palaces or Asylum Prisons," and intended for the eyes of members of the State Legislature, he made a strong plea. He not only questioned the ability of the medical officers to treat the mentally ill and cited poor recovery rates to prove his point, but he also gave account of an instance in which a capable nurse was obstructed from caring for patients although she had previously been successful in effecting the recovery of apparently hopeless cases. He contrasted this nurse with a hospital physician who, through medical ignorance, had caused the death of many insane women. Nine years later, in 1908, Clifford Beers published "A Mind That Found Itself," in which he described the abuses suffered by patients in mental hospitals. Among the letters received by Beers in response to the manuscript of his book was one from William James, the last paragraph of which is as true today as when it was written in 1907:

"Nowhere is there massed together as much suffering as in the asylums. Nowhere is there so much sodden routine and fatalistic insensibility as in those who have to treat it. Nowhere is an ideal treatment more costly. The officials in charge grow resigned to the conditions under which they have to labor. They cannot plead their cause as an auxiliary organization can plead it for them. Public opinion is too glad to remain ignorant. As mediator between officials, patients, and the public conscience, a society such as you sketch is absolutely required and the sooner it gets under way the better. Sincerely yours, William James." (22)

The sodden routine and fatalistic insensibility to which James refers is the damaging product of the incurability myth within the walls of mental hospitals. The stigma which it places on the mentally ill, in conjunction with exaggeration of the role of heredity, is as effective as the medieval belief in demon possession in denying them their rights not only to the means of recovery but to decent living standards.

Social progress is usually made through the organized efforts of those who themselves are the victims of deprivation. The very essence of mental illness, however, is an incapacity to get along with other people, hence organization behind a leader is impossible. The friends or relatives of the mentally ill are equally immobilized through fear of stigmatizing themselves.

The damaging effect of the incurability myth is a thought provoking revelation of the sensitivity of the mentally ill to the attitudes of those about them. Failure to recognize this factor has inhibited psychiatric progress for over a hundred years and to the present day underlies the low standards of many mental hospitals. It is disturbing to compare the recovery rates of the Worcester State Hospital decade by decade during the Century of Progress 1833-1933 (see Fig. 3 in Chapter V). One may contend that this decline in recovery rates from 45% to 4% is an artefact, but the fact remains that it accompanied not only a diminution in treatment efforts, but also a reduction of the patients' standard of living.

We cannot escape the conclusion that our society had, until very recently, become less and less concerned about the fate of its mentally ill during the very years that its standard of living was increasing at an ever more rapid tempo.

IV

**Personality and
Scientific Outlook in
Psychiatric Leadership**

The irony of the psychiatric profession today is that it sub-
scribes to the great therapeutic value of dynamic psychiatry in
mental illness yet fails to apply its principles in the care of those
who are in the greatest need: namely psychotic patients legally
confined in our mental hospitals. This failure is largely based on
indecision as to the curability of psychosis. The stigma of hopelessness associated with psychosis in the public mind is, to be
sure, sorely lamented by psychiatrists. Nevertheless by their
own actions they contribute to the stigma by handling psychotic
patients as intractable prisoners, incapable of benefiting from *any*
treatment. The very fact that such a method of handling pre-
dominates throughout the world strongly suggests that psychiatrists themselves harbor belief in the very stigma they would
remove from society by public education. Such a discrepancy
between what is preached and what is practiced does not be-
speak cynicism in the profession but rather a time lag in the
spread of knowledge from research and teaching centers which
do the preaching to the outlying mental hospitals which receive
the vast majority of patients.

As so often happens in science, recently acquired perspectives
turn out to be a more precise form of very old perspectives which
were left undeveloped. Those who have come to rely on certain
habits in giving service, who are not actively engaged in research,
and who no longer preserve an open mind in areas in which their

own habits come into question, naturally resist accepting the new and devaluate it on the grounds that it was "old stuff" long ago and "nothing came of it."

Psychiatrists cannot afford to forget that unprejudiced open-minded effort to discover any and every means for supplying the personal needs and arousing the dormant faculties of psychotic patients was the very purpose which gave birth to psychiatry as a profession in the first place.

With Pinel's twofold discovery, over 150 years ago, that organic lesions could not be found in most instances of insanity, and that recovery could be achieved through effort invested in supplying personal needs and arousing dormant faculties—which he named moral treatment—psychiatry came into existence not solely as a humanitarian reform but also as a successful therapeutic enterprise.

Pinel's report on this discovery, "Treatise On Insanity," was first made available to the English-speaking world in 1806. His account of how he learned of the curability of insanity from a layman is a masterpiece of open-mindedness in psychiatry:

"Of the knowledge to be derived from books on the treatment of insanity I felt the most extreme insufficiency. Desirous of better information, I resolved to examine for myself the facts that were presented to my attention; and forgetting the empty honours of my titular distinction as a physician, I viewed the scene that was opened to me with the eyes of common sense and unprejudiced observation. I saw a great number of maniacs assembled together, and submitted to a regular system of discipline. Their disorders presented an endless variety of character; but their discordant movements were regulated on the part of the governor (lay superintendent) by the greatest possible skill, and even extravagance and disorder were marshalled into order and harmony. I then discovered, that insanity was curable in many instances, by mildness of treatment and attention to the mind exclusively, and when coercion was indispensable, that it might be very effectively applied without corporal indignity. To give all their value to the facts which I had the opportunity of observing, I made it an object of interest to trace their alliance

to the functions of the understanding. To assist me in this
inquiry, I attentively perused the best writers upon modern
pneumatology (defined in Webster as the science of the nature
and functions of mind and soul), as well as those authors who
have written on the influence of the passions upon the pathology
of the human mind. The laws of the human economy considered
in reference to insanity as well as other diseases, impressed me
with admiration of their uniformity, and I saw, with wonder,
the resources of nature when left to herself, or skillfully assisted
in her efforts. My faith in pharmaceutic preparations was gradually lessened, and my skepticism went at length so far, as to
induce me never to have recourse to them, until moral remedies
had completely failed. . . .

"Attention to these principles of moral treatment alone will,
frequently, not only lay the foundation of, but complete a cure,
while neglect of them may exasperate each succeeding paroxysm,
till, at length, the disease becomes established, continued in its
form and incurable. The successful application of moral regimen
exclusively gives great weight to the supposition, that, in the
majority of instances, there is no organic lesion of the brain nor
of the cranium." (32)

The effectiveness of moral treatment was first made widely
known to the medical profession in America by a physician
whose open-mindedness also included the capacity to adopt a
layman's conception of the treatment of insanity. Dr. Eli Todd,
fearing his own susceptibility to insanity from the knowledge
that his father and sister died insane, acquainted himself with
the philosophy and method of treatment developed by the
Quaker layman, William Tuke, at the York Retreat in England.
Dr. Todd was not a Quaker but an avowed religious skeptic who
subscribed to the philosophies which gave rise to the French
Revolution. Nevertheless he expended all his efforts to have a
hospital established in Connecticut along the lines of the York
Retreat.

Dr. Todd entered the practice of medicine in 1790 at the
age of 20. It was in 1812 that he began playing an active role
in behalf of obtaining moral treatment for the insane. In that

year he was appointed to the Connecticut Medical Society's committee for investigating the condition of the insane. In 1822 he succeeded in organizing a Society for the Relief of the Insane, and in 1824 he was appointed director of the newly founded Hartford Retreat which was sponsored by the Connecticut Medical Society largely because of Dr. Todd's efforts. Thus it happened that at a time when England's physicians scoffed at William Tuke's York Retreat, an American medical society actually sponsored a hospital patterned and named after it.

Dr. Todd had a "profound sympathy for the insane which stamped all his views and conduct." (25) He was acutely aware of the sensitivity and needs of psychotic patients. His view was: "In their whole intercourse with society, their spirits are wounded by a sneer or a jest. . . . The force of their disease is augmented from day to day, and at last suicide or confirmed insanity is the result of accumulated though imaginary insanity." (26) He also commented on the uniqueness of mental suffering: "All other sufferers seek relief from their sufferings and successfully appeal to the kindly feelings of man for sympathy and aid. But unlike all others, the maniac who most needs tenderness and care, is neglected, because he shuns the care and tenderness which he needs, repels the hand stretched out for his relief and would fain bar the door of charity against himself." (44)

Dr. Todd's system of treatment, in the words of Dr. Charles W. Page, "was not a code of rules for subordinates to enforce, no austere, remote, authority, but personal devotion and painstaking labor with his patients—that method of true leadership in a good cause which always commands respect and insures success." (27)

Dr. Samuel B. Woodward, in his report on Dr. Todd's management of the Hartford Retreat, made the following observations: "In respect to the moral and intellectual treatment, the first business of a physician is to gain the patient's entire confidence. With this in view he is treated with the greatest kindness, however violent his conduct may be,—is allowed all the liberty his case admits of, and is made to understand, if he is still capable of reflection, that, so far from having arrived at a mad-house where he is to be confined, he has come to a pleasant and cheerful residence where all kindness and attention will be shown him, and where every means will be used for his recovery to health. In no case is deception employed or allowed; on the contrary the greatest frankness as well as kindness form a part of the moral treatment. His case is explained to him, and he is made to understand, as far as possible, the reason why the treatment to which he is being subjected has become necessary." (28)

In Dr. Todd's own view his method was based on the law of kindness, mental philosophy, and physiology. He built on the experience of both Pinel and Tuke and combined medical, dietetic, and psychological treatments. Under his direction the Hartford Retreat became the model after which so many American mental hospitals were patterned during the first half of the nineteenth century. His personality was also in many of its qualities the prototype of the moral therapists who followed in his steps. Qualities ascribed to him such as benevolence, kindliness, cheerfulness, ingenuousness, and magnanimous altruism were also ascribed to Drs. Samuel B. Woodward, Isaac Ray, Amariah Brigham, Thomas Kirkbride, Luther Bell, and John S. Butler. They shared a common interest in patients first and foremost as *people*. Their writings all contain accounts of their philosophically minded sympathetic investigations of their patients' state of mind. Indeed they did not seem to even think in terms of universally applicable disease processes but rather operated on the general assumption that every patient was a special case and that their duty as physicians was to use every possible means to enhance the welfare and self-respect of patients individually and collectively.

One of the clearest examples of individual psychotherapy as practiced by the moral therapists is that of Dr. John S. Butler of the Boston State Hospital (1839-1842) and the Hartford Retreat (1843-1872), as noted by Charles W. Page: "It was his common practice to dig deeply into the family and personal history of his patients, to establish, if possible, a connection between their mental disorder and some accident or error in their lives. And this he did, not only that he might the more intelligently treat the patient, but that he might be able to give the patient and friends, in case of recovery, such warnings that subsequent attacks might be prevented or at least guarded against." (29)

One of Dr. Butler's principles of psychotherapy was to use positive propositions and never negative ones. It was his claim that all destructive patients responded to persevering efforts in the direction of discovering and respecting their preferences. A specific instance, in the words of Dr. Charles W. Page: "He did not depend upon restraint or seclusion to arrest destructive habits. If a woman tore her dress he aimed to stimulate her self-respect and pride. He would provide her with a new dress conspicuous for its pretty pattern or bright colors. And when he saw her thus clad he would express pride and pleasure, complimenting her on her improved appearance." (30)

Dr. Butler, it is significant to note, was stimulated to enter the field of mental medicine by witnessing, while a general practitioner, the favorable outcome of patients treated by Dr. Woodward at the Worcester State Hospital. He visited the hospital frequently, and as a result of his great interest and avid study of patients he was recommended by Dr. Woodward for directorship of the Boston State Hospital (then Boston City Hospital for the Insane) in 1839. Here Dr. Butler applied the methods of moral treatment in the care of long-term chronically insane patients, the results of which won the acclaim of Charles Dickens as related in Chapter II.

Without benefit of modern psychological discoveries, these pioneer psychiatrists provided a high standard of treatment simply by acting on the philosophical assumption that the healthy mind could understand and influence the sick mind for the better. To them it appeared self-evident that every aspect of hospital life had a bearing on the issue of the patients' mental condition. They believed that success depended on constant vigilance to the needs of patients. At the same time they were aware that disappointment was to be expected in patients with general paresis or other psychoses, accompanied by signs of organic brain disease. Such disappointment did not, nevertheless, undermine their faith in the effectiveness of moral treatment with the majority of patients. It is not unlikely though, that accumulation of patients with undetected brain disease had something to do with the final decline of moral treatment.

From the time of Dr. Todd's demonstration of the success of moral treatment at the Hartford Retreat in the 1820's to the 1840's, a dozen or so small hospitals were founded and a score or so physicians had become proficient in the application of moral treatment.

In 1841 a new personality came into a position of leadership where the care of the insane was concerned. In that year Dorothea Dix discovered that large numbers of insane people were suffering unbelievable abuse in the jails and almshouses of Massachusetts. She also learned of the humane treatment patients were receiving at the three small mental hospitals in that state. From the moment she learned of such suffering and its remedy, her soul would know no rest until every abused insane individual was a patient in a mental hospital. With fanatic singleness of purpose she set out on her amazing career of accomplishing reform by direct appeal to state legislatures. She was rapidly successful in achieving the results she demanded, namely the construction of new, and expansion of already existing, mental hospitals. The Worcester State Hospital was enlarged, as previously noted, in 1843 against Dr. Woodward's wishes by an act of the Massachusetts legislature. Two more hospitals of larger capacity were built in the 1850's. This was only a start. Miss Dix was not content to sit back until every state of the Union, province of Canada, and nation of Europe had provided hospital space sufficient to house all the insane.

Her immense emphasis on eliminating gross abuse of the insane had the most unfortunate effect of driving into the background any serious consideration of the requirements to be met in securing positive treatment. The inundation of mental hospitals with long-standing chronic cases ruined moral treatment. Neither the chronic cases transferred to the hospitals from jails, almshouses, cellars, and attics nor the new cases of recently acquired insanity could benefit from the art and therapeutic know-how which had been learned by moral therapists since the time of Pinel and Tuke.

In the surge of public remorse and·pity aroused by Miss Dix, the reform movement jumped to the conclusion that elimination of abuse *in itself* would result in the recovery of the curable. With adoption of the negative function of preventing abuse, mental hospitals became, in the words of the aforementioned Franklin B. Sanborn ". . . in too many instances . . . centers of intellectual indolence or of semi-political intrigue; to whose busy and well-paid medical men new ideas were irksome, and any forward step in the care of their patients or the guidance of public opinion was the familiar story of goodness going to seed and planting the surrounding fields with a growth which was not goodness, or at least was a degenerate and reverting form thereof." (35)

Dorothea Dix lived to see her goal of placing all insane in mental hospitals largely reached, but, again in the words of Sanborn, "for the needs of the situation *which her own heroic activity had so largely created* she had neither the vital force nor the special knowledge and discrimination required." (35) Nevertheless she functioned as a self-appointed inspector of mental hospitals. Her imperious manner, rigid opinions, and attitude of censorship introduced a new element into hospital psychiatry, namely the element of fault-finding, critical, and punishing authority. Her great political influence with state legislatures gave her considerable voice in the selection of physicians for superintendencies of mental hospitals. It is not unlikely that she was largely responsible for the emphasis which came to be placed on protecting patients against any and all mishaps and the stagnation of hospital life which resulted from it. Dix's goal of moving all patients from almshouses and jails to mental hospitals was never completely accomplished. As late as 1900, there were some 900 patients in the almshouses of Massachusetts, the state in which she began her reform.

In 1904 the State Care Act was passed which completely relieved the towns of paying for their patients' support in state hospitals. This was followed by another large influx of patients into mental hospitals from jails and almshouses.

Thus it happened that the much needed and long venerated social reform, initiated by Dorothea Dix, collided with and brought to a halt a successful approach to the psychological treatment of mental illness.

During the many years this movement was taking place a new type of psychiatrist appeared. He replaced the optimistic, enthusiastic therapeutic orientation of the moral therapist with the prohibitive, restrictive, watchful, mishap-avoiding orientation of the administrative custodian of the insane. Interest in treatment was replaced by interest in diagnosis, legal questions of responsibility, and brain pathology.

A little more than a decade after Dorothea Dix began her campaign for building and enlarging mental hospitals, leadership in American psychiatry passed to the superintendent of the largest state hospital in America—the Utica State Hospital in New York. Dr. John P. Gray was appointed superintendent in 1854, and in 1855 he assumed editorship of the American Journal of Insanity. He held both posts for 30 years. He insisted that insanity was always due to physical lesion, and became the greatest single influence in swinging psychiatry back to the pre-Pinel position.

Dr. Gray was the first to introduce the microscope into American mental hospitals for the study of post-mortem material in the search for the etiology of mental diseases. He also took the role of leadership in changing mental hospital organization to treat the mentally ill patient as *physically* ill. He placed great emphasis on rest, diet, proper room temperature, and ventilation. One of his accomplishments was the invention of a rotary fan for the ventilation of the Utica State Hospital. Dr. Gray was also an authority on legal psychiatry and was in much demand by the courts. He refused to accept deviant behavior such as dypsomania, kleptomania, and moral insanity as psychiatric entities. To consider them as such he deplored as unjustifiable shielding of depravity and crime. He made a sharp distinction between mind and brain, categorically stating that insanity "is simply a bodily disease in which the mind is disturbed more or less profoundly, because the brain is involved in the sickness either primarily or secondarily. The mind is not, itself, ever diseased. It is incapable of disease or of its final consequence, death." (17) He specified in particular that "no moral or intellectual operations of the mind induce insanity apart from physical disease." (18) Dr. Gray was a man of firm religious conviction. He apparently made no distinction between mind and immortal soul and could therefore not accept the idea of mind being susceptible to sickness. Thus his religious belief and his faith in the microscope combined to support a materialistic conception of mental illness.

Dr. Gray's legalistic skill and forceful personality made him the dominant American psychiatrist of the latter half of the nineteenth century. The high point of his career was probably his success as an expert witness in proving to the satisfaction of the jury that Guiteau, President Garfield's assassin, was not insane. All told, he was successful in winning acceptance of his main contentions that insanity is due to physical disease and that "crime and depravity" are not psychiatric conditions. Although in the treatment of the insane he relied on rest and diet to aid nature in the cure of the underlying physical disease assumed to be present, he subscribed to what he termed moral treatment, in the form of amusements, recreation, and occupation as useful adjuncts. This was a complete reversal of the original concept of moral treatment as a direct influence on the patient's mental condition. Dr. Gray's views on the nature of insanity precluded any effort toward psychological understanding of patients. He was "uncompromising, unyielding, and in a certain sense coercive in his views of psychiatry," (23) says his biographer. It is of significance that when the "National Association for the Protection of the Insane and Prevention of Insanity" was organized in the 1880's, it picked Dr. Gray as its first object of attack. He also drew the criticism of the British psychiatrist, Dr. G. A. Tucker, for arguing that the majority of patients at the Utica State Hospital were allowed out of doors, on the basis of the number reported to have gone outdoors on a particular date; Tucker pointed out that this was the very day the members of the Association of Superintendents of Insane Asylums were visiting the hospital.

Dr. Gray, it would appear, aroused a great deal of antagonism with his dogmatic narrow view of mental illness and emphasis on administrative efficiency. Nevertheless he is also remembered for abolishing seclusion and restraint, for increasing the freedom of patients, and for increasing the number of attendants in order to give patients more personal care. He was also mindful of the role of stress—physical stress that is—in the causation of insanity, especially those stresses following childbirth. He admitted that emotional states such as prolonged grief could cause insanity but only by way of producing structural changes secondary to insufficient rest and nourishment. He could not conceive of insanity as a disease unless caused by physical lesion: "If the mind could so contemplate its own operations, its intellectual conceptions, its moral ideas, its emotional states, as to pass into a state of insanity, as it passes into a state of joy or grief, or jealousy, then insanity is no disease." (19) Here Dr. Gray revealed the basic dilemma of a psychiatry attempting to hue to the line of materialistic medicine in forming its attitude toward, and hence treatment of, psychosis. The question became one in which the patient's responsibility and culpability hinged on whether his behavior was thought to be the result of physical lesion or not. If his behavior was due to a lesion, then the psychotic patient had a right to be served and waited upon as a sick person. If not, he was deemed responsible for his acts and deserving of punishment. Thus from the point of view of materialistic medicine the medical man should logically disclaim having any role to play with respect to behavior not due to physical disease. Psychiatry could not take this position: if it did so it would be a specialty without patients, for the rising specialty of neurology was preempting the field of organic diseases of the nervous system.

It is curious why the idea of mental illness without physical lesion was so offensive to Dr. Gray and colleagues who entered psychiatry during the latter half of the last century. For it was belief in the psychological origin of mental illness which had originally inspired physicians to specialize in the treatment of mental illness and to found the profession of psychiatry. It would appear that the scientifically oriented psychiatrist of the latter decades of the century felt dutybound to adhere to the neat logic of physical science and to discard the metaphysical theories of the unity of man derived from natural philosophy, upon which moral treatment of the earlier decades was based. Scientific psychiatry eliminated moral treatment as a definitive therapy and retained it in diluted form as a diversionary adjunct to medical treatment persued in the empty climate of custodial care.

Recovery rates decreased steadily with the passage of each decade. Mental hospital directors generally sought to obscure this fact and continued to support the contention that insanity was curable even though they had come to regard it as a physical disease of unknown etiology. They appeared to believe, along with Dr. Gray, that rest, diet, and diversion was a rational program of treatment. Somehow at that time the concept of insanity as a physical disease meant that it was relatively easy to treat and that the special efforts of the pioneer psychiatrists to meet the psychological needs of patients were not necessary. This overly optimistic view was unfortunately accompanied by the low standards of care. Indeed in many instances propagation of such optimism amounted to being a cynical cover-up of culpable neglect and abuse of patients. Mental hospitals had become as reprehensible as the jails and almshouses from which Dorothea Dix had labored so long to remove patients. And fittingly it was an old friend of hers who undertook to reform professional attitudes on the subject of easy curability. He was Dr. Pliny Earle, superintendent of the Northampton State Hospital, Massachusetts.

Dr. Earle's psychiatric career, like that of Butler, Ray, and Kirkbride began in the 1830's and ended in the 1880's. It included both the moral treatment era and the physical disease era. Like Dr. Butler, Earle was inspired to enter the field of psychiatry by Dr. Woodward's work at the Worcester State

Hospital. Dr. Earle took special interest in psychiatry in medical
school. His graduating thesis (1837) was "The Causes, Duration,
Termination, and Moral Treatment of Insanity." After finishing
medical school he went to England and France where he observed the care of patients by Tuke's followers at the York Retreat, and by Pinel's followers at the Bicêtre and the Salpêtrière
in Paris. After his return to America he was appointed resident
physician to the Friends' Retreat at Frankford, Pennsylvania, in
1840. Here he pursued the methods of moral treatment and
eliminated bloodletting and drastic medicinal treatments which
had become the practice in that hospital from the influence of
Dr. Rush.

Within the framework of moral treatment he included psychological study of his patients' mental state. Like other physicians
of that day he was versed in phrenology and familiar with the
phenomena of mesmerism. He was impressed with the practical
value of the former from personal experience. In 1842 he wrote:
"The examination of Stephen Earle's head (Dr. Earle's brother)
and of mine by L. N. Fowler did more to convince me of the
practical utility of phrenology—not to say of its truth as a
science—than anything else that I ever saw, read, or heard.
Stephen was told what I believe he might have been rather
than what he is. But, for myself, I doubt if any of my nearest
relatives or most intimate friends could have given a more
accurate synopsis of my character." (36)

Dr. Earle also constructed psychodynamic formulations of
the patients' mental conflicts in the anatomic-psychic language
of phrenology. The following account of one of his patients at
Frankford gives some idea of his effort to understand patients:

"He is unsettled, restless, and constantly worrying about
something. His Conscientiousness thinks that the buttons of his
vest, which are covered with plain black 'lasting,' are too gay.
His Reverence is in an inexplicable quandary in regard to a
copy of Scott's Family Bible, which it and Acquisitiveness procured. After the purchase, Reverence, reading the commentary,
became dissatisfied, and openly promulgated dissatisfaction.
Hereupon Destructiveness advised to burn the book. "That would

be a wise expedient for the commentary,' remarked Reverence, 'but for the text it would be sacrilegious, and to separate them is impossible.' Benevolence, hearing the colloquy, proposed to give the book away. 'And contaminate somebody else, eh' cried Reverence, holding up both hands in astonishment. At this point Secretiveness whispered that, if he had the management, he would box the book up, and hide it among the lumber of the garret. 'And thus contaminate posterity,' exclaimed Reverence and Philprogenitiveness, simultaneously. Here the consultation ended, and poor Reverence can see no way out of the dilemma. Acquisitiveness and Conscientiousness have long been in combat. The former came into possession of some notes of hand, and, on the day they were to be renewed, sat down composedly to cast compound interest on the several sums. At this moment Conscientiousness came in, declaring that Acquisitiveness was doing wrong. 'Bigot!' cried Acquisitiveness: 'You are always meddling with other people's affairs.' 'But you outrage justice,' said Conscientiousness in a tone which showed he was spurred on by his neighbor Firmness. 'Grumble and growl away,' retorted Acquisitiveness. 'I shall stick to my text, and pocket the compound interest.' The field was won by the last speaker. Conscientiousness retreated, but has kept up a kind of predatory warfare ever since." (37)

Although Dr. Earle apparently understood the role of conflict in insanity, there is no evidence that he sought to relieve it through direct discussion of mental content and personal history with patients singly or in groups as did Dr. Butler. Quite to the contrary, Dr. Earle relied mostly on lectures on a variety of subjects and demonstrations of scientific experiments to mobilize healthy mental activity. No doubt his experience as a school teacher influenced his choice of method. He also carried out a program of full activity including entertainment, recreation, and work.

In 1844 Dr. Earle was appointed the first medical director of the Bloomingdale Hospital (now Westchester Division of the New York Hospital) which had been under lay management since its founding in 1821. Here Dr. Earle further elaborated his

program of treatment but met with disappointment in attempting
to persuade patients to work. They were of the wealthy classes
and objected to working on the grounds that they paid their
keep. It is not unlikely that his short term of office at Bloomingdale—five years—was the result of disagreements arising over his
efforts to enforce his policy on work for patients. In 1847, while
at Bloomingdale, Dr. Earle discovered the first case of general
paralysis to be diagnosed as such in America. Among the cases
of this disease (established to be incurable by Calmeil), diagnosed by Dr. Earle, one patient recovered who was perfectly
well ten years after his discharge from the hospital.

On leaving Bloomingdale in 1849 Dr. Earle went on an
extended tour of German mental hospitals. In the course of this
tour he came in contact with concepts which held insanity to be
a hopeless physical disease. He also saw many more cases of
general paresis which was regarded by some German psychiatrists
at that time not as a disease entity by itself but as an end stage
of insanity in general. Dr. Earle was greatly impressed with
German administrative efficiency and discipline, especially where
it had put into effect an extensive work-program for patients.

On his return to America, Dr. Earle's expectation of being
appointed superintendent of one of the newly established mental
hospitals did not materialize. He took up residence in his home
village of Leicester, Massachusetts, where he remained in professional inactivity for about three years. He then went to New
York City and opened an office as a consultant on mental disorders. While in New York he was appointed to a committee of
medical visitors to the city asylum on Blackwell's Island where
he saw still more cases of general paralysis and the evil results
of hospital mismanagement. He remained in New York for but
a short time and then travelled in the South and to Cuba. In
1854 he returned to Leicester where he remained in retirement
for 10 years. During this time he studied annual reports from
mental hospitals all over the world. In the words of his biographer: "He bided his time with some impatience and not without
months and days of despondency. He lived at Leicester, in a
small house, and amid humble duties of one sort or another."

(37) The reason for his despondency was presumably his disappointment of seeing physicians less qualified than himself appointed as superintendents of the many mental hospitals built during those years. This is not certain, however, for he was subject to periods of depression throughout his life as were other members of his family. There is some evidence also that his mood swings went in the other direction. His biographer noted: "Punning, indeed, in its many forms was carried by him to an excess. It was one kind of grammatical exercise in which he long delighted."

In 1864 Dr. Earle was finally appointed superintendent of the Northampton State Hospital in Massachusetts. Here, in marked contrast to the wealthy patients at Bloomingdale Hospital, he had charge of 450 patients, practically all of the "pauper classes," nine-tenths of whom were long-standing chronic cases transferred to Northampton to make room for new admissions to the other state hospitals. Nevertheless Dr. Earle pursued the program of moral treatment as developed by him at Bloomingdale. At Northampton he had one advantage at least: there was no objection to his ideas on manual work for patients. He also revamped the administration of the hospital by introducing methods for achieving business efficiency and discipline which he had admired in Germany. Yet in spite of his respect for his patients' love of beauty (he hung over 1,500 pictures in the hospital), in spite of his giving lectures and directing recreational activities more than 300 evenings a year, and in spite of his success in persuading a majority of his patients to work, he found his recovery rates to be much lower than those reported by his contemporaries. He knew that many of his fellow superintendents were political appointees who had no training in psychiatry and no interest in patients. He was also fully aware that none of the other state hospitals had a program of moral treatment remotely approaching his own.

Dr. Earle was a deeply religious Quaker. He was also overly modest, scrupulously honest, and very frugal. He despised ostentation of any kind. He disapproved thoroughly of vindictiveness, but there was one issue which aroused his righteous anger and about which he could not remain silent. He abhorred the current practice of building large "palace hospitals" which he considered to be extravagant shams covering up neglect of patients. From his point of view the rationale for building such hospitals was based on the fallacy of easy curability. He therefore set out to prove through presentation of statistical data that cures were much less frequent than commonly believed at that time. In his own opinion his statistical studies were "an important agent in stimulating the minds of philanthropists to seek—and in several notable instances to adopt—other methods for the custody and care of a large part of the insane than that of collecting them in expensive and unwieldy curative institutions." (10)

Unfortunately Dr. Earle's studies had the opposite effect. They promoted extreme pessimism in psychiatry and almost complete cessation of treatment efforts. Yet the very data on which he based his conclusions form a basis for a far more optimistic outlook than is commonly held today. These data are presented and discussed more fully in Chapter V.

In the case of Pliny Earle, to compare him with Dorothea Dix, the "goodness that went to seed" lay in his interpretation of his statistical work to the effect that incurability was an attribute of mental illness itself. His intention was to destroy complacency and bring about sound methods of treatment. He showed that recovery rates were higher in the early decades of the nineteenth century than in the 1870's and '80's. He pointed out that breach of the principle that no more than 200 patients should be cared for in one institution was partly responsible for the poorer results of the later years. Likewise he demonstrated certain fallacies in the statistical reports of the early superintendents which had resulted in some exaggeration of their recovery rates and showed that relapses of recovered cases further reduced the proportion of "true" recoveries. Through his tenacious efforts he was able to convince himself and others that recoveries had been less frequent in the past than had been realized and that they were becoming even less frequent. This insistence on the infrequency of recovery and the statement that the disease itself was becoming more incurable obscured the fact that recoveries were not only possible but had been as frequent as 70% of admissions in well-run institutions.

Dr. Earle was not only successful in changing the outlook of physicians on the curability of insanity, he was also largely responsible for an important change in the attitude of state administrators regarding the functions of superintendents of mental hospitals. His own great frugality, love of arithmetic (he was also the hospital's treasurer), knowledge of farming, and ability to persuade patients to work enabled him not only to operate the hospital more economically than any other superintendent, but to show a profit. The following account by Franklin B. Sanborn portrays in detail Dr. Earle's success as an administrator:

"At the end of Dr. Earle's fourth year (at Northampton) not only had the valuation of the hospital property increased by nearly $30,000 since he came, but the trustees were able to say, 'For the first time since the founding of the hospital we have passed a year without borrowing money,' and they closed the year with a balance of near $10,000 in hand. This balance went on increasing—though often drawn upon for other than current expenses—until when Dr. Earle resigned in 1885, it stood at $34,000; while the valuation figures had gone up from $272,000 in 1864 to more than $440,000 in 1885. This gain came from the high cultivation of the enlarged farm, the better labor of the employed patients, the systematic handling of all expenditure, and for a time the increased income from private patients.

"By the prudent management of the hospital, Dr. Earle disarmed criticism on the economic side, and made his establishment popular with the legislature and the State authorities, who had been accustomed to see it a frequent applicant for appropriations, not only for repairs and new building (as was the case with other hospitals), but for deficiencies in its current expense. To meet the lack of a working capital, which every new hospital feels, the Board of State Charities, in accord with Dr. Earle, procured advance payments for nine-tenths of the State patients there (which was perfectly safe, since they were permanent boarders), and this enabled him to make cash purchases, and thereby reduce the current cost. This he also reduced materially by introducing the system of distributing supplies which he had seen practised in frugal Germany; each person employed being made accountable for the articles delivered upon his request, and thus becoming more careful against waste or theft,—the latter by no means unknown formerly in such establishments. In this way he became a model for other hospitals to follow, as they gradually did, but not until some of them had suffered from extravagance and peculation so as to attract public notice." (38)

The phenomenon of a mathematically minded, hard-headed business man with knowledge of agriculture, being at the same time a wise physician and skilled psychiatrist, was indeed fortunate for the Commonwealth in a financial way. It was unfortunate, however, that his penurious qualities were the ones most admired by the state administrators and that they helped to establish a precedent of choosing men for superintendencies who had these qualities.

Some of Dr. Earle's opinions about insanity provide clues which suggest why he placed such stress on its incurability. First, he regarded insanity as a mystery. He said: "The disorder—not to say 'disease,' inasmuch as disease implies the possibility of death—in its essential nature, and even in its relation to the conduct and the practical ability of those who are affected with it, is an inexplicable mystery to persons who are constantly surrounded by it, and who are consequently better informed than any others in regard to it." (39) Second, he discounted the idea that the insane suffer unhappiness. He even contended that depressed patients went through the motions of being sad in a machine-like fashion but did not really feel it. He explained away the suffering of insanity: "I do not forget, but am most free to acknowledge, that the worst wards of a hospital of this kind present a sad spectacle, even to persons familiarized with it—a very sad spectacle to anyone to whom it is an unaccustomed sight. But this aspect is the consequence of mental impairment and bodily deterioration, and is no evidence of unhappiness on the part of the patients. The observer derives his judgment from his own feelings and emotions, not from the mental and moral condition of the persons around him, which, particularly if he be a casual visitor, he cannot accurately know." (40)

Yet Dr. Earle was in no way a callous man. Apparently he did not believe insanity to be accompanied by suffering because he, like Dr. Gray, equated mind with immortal soul and did not believe it was susceptible to disease, as indicated in the following statements: "Were the arguments for the hypothesis that in insanity the mind itself is diseased tenfold more numerous than they are, and more weighty, I could not accept them. My ideas of the human mind are such that I cannot hold for a moment that it can be diseased, as we understand disease. That implies death as a final consequence, but Mind is eternal. In its very essence and structure (to use the terms we apply to matter), in its elemental composition and its organization, it was created for immortality. Consequently, it is superior to the bodily structure and beyond the scope of the wear and tear and disorganization and final destruction of the mortal part of our being." (40) "The longer I live, the more I am impressed with a belief in the all-controlling supremacy of mind over matter, of the far-reaching, mysterious power of the divine intelligence within, and of the limited bounds of present knowledge, compared with what is to be known when mind shall have thrown off its fetters of clay. Science is proud, even presumptuous; but how much cause for humility in the fact that it cannot trace one particle of its knowledge upward, through effects, to the original cause and center of all things! Science is lost at once in the mazes of uncertainty and ignorance, whenever it attempts to fathom mind itself." (41)

Apparently Dr. Earle's concept of the incurability of insanity had a special meaning to him in terms of his own philosophy of life. There is little doubt that he felt a great affinity for the insane, for he devoted his life to their care, never married, and was a victim of depression himself. His biographer said: "Consecration is the right word to describe his care for the insane. With all his worldly prudence and common sense, and notwithstanding his broad toleration of theological differences, he was from the first, and essentially, a religious man, governed in all the important actions of life by a sense of religious duty and that regard for the fatherhood of God and the brotherhood of man, which the small sect of his family and forefathers especially cherishes. Of the narrowness of the Quaker church he had nothing; of the profound instinct of divine guidance and the worth of the human soul he had much. In the growing strength of materialism among scientific men and physicians, he still maintained the spiritual and immortal nature of our minds, and could have said with Shakespeare, 'I think more nobly of the soul, and no way approve their opinion', . . It required some courage and firm religious conviction to adhere to this noble opinion during the latter half of the passing century." (40)

Another aspect of Dr. Earle's personality is described by his biographer as follows: "One of the chief qualifications of a superintendent for such a difficult position was as marked in Dr. Earle as in any of the hundred superintendents and directors of hospitals and asylums whom I have personally known in an experience now covering 35 years (written in 1898)—his strictness of discipline, both for patients and attendants. This, which sometimes passed for unkindness, and was really exacting now and then, was the truest kindness when the real interest of all persons was considered. The inflexible justice of a most kindly nature thus displayed itself, often at the cost of much pain to the doctor himself." (42)

There is no doubt that in one sense Dr. Earle took excellent care of his patients. They were not only better fed but had a lower death rate than those of any other hospital in the country. Also they had the busiest and most interesting community life of any hospital at that time. Nevertheless there is some suggestion that there was a connection between the fact of a high proportion of working patients, low discharge rates, and the excellent financial condition of the hospital. Indeed Dr. Earle's biographer makes the following statement: "It was to this steady but not compulsory discipline of labor that the financial success of the hospital was due in great part; and, though the record of recoveries at Northampton showed small numbers, because

the cases were so largely chronic, yet there were many un-
recorded *virtual* recoveries—patients who, while still insane, were
capable of self-support and self-direction under kindly super-
vision." (43) It might be said that Dr. Earle behaved like an
overprotective father who fostered dependency and could not
countenance patients leaving the family fold.

Dr. Earle's philosophy and methods of patient-care in mental
hospitals are by no means merely an historical curiosity. He was
regarded as the model superintendent by the Massachusetts
Board of State Charities, and through that body he had an
influence on the makeup of mental hospitals which has lasted
up to the present day. Dr. John P. Gray exerted a similar influence on the development of New York state hospitals.

It is over 60 years since Dorothea Dix, Dr. Pliny Earle, and
Dr. John P. Gray died and left behind them the mark of their
particular personalities on the care of the mentally ill. Since
that time revolutionary changes have taken place in the whole
of society, in medicine and in psychiatry itself *as a science.* Yet
in *practice,* psychiatry has had little or no effect on the care
of patients in mental hospitals. Indeed the perspectives and
methods of Dix, Earle, and Gray have become a deeply ingrained
tradition.

As long ago as 1901 Dr. Charles W. Page, superintendent of
the Middletown State Hospital in Connecticut, gently reminded
the psychiatric profession of the need to return to the principles
of the early moral treatment era:

"It is now more than half a century since Butler formulated
in his mind those tenets, or methods, the application, or execution
of which gave him a prominent position as a specialist in mental
disease. This period has been marked not only by great changes
in the social condition of our population, but most surprising
advances have been made in science and the arts.

"Medicine, in some branches at least, has been rewritten
upon a basis of comparatively recent science. In keeping with
the general trend of business affairs, lunatic hospitals have undergone changes. They have rapidly increased in numbers and
vastly expanded in size. In their laudable desire for a scientific

standing they vie with each other in providing laboratory facilities. Medical officers also are burdened with executive obligations, and ambitious ones must devote much time to pathological questions. With the pressure of these new, interesting and important considerations, painstaking personal efforts with individual patients are in danger of being neglected. And yet the power of the mind over the body, and the laws of sympathy which, unfortunately, cannot be stated in scientific terms, have undergone no changes, and will ever respond to right application.

"Is there not an obvious moral to be drawn from a review of Butler's life-work, namely our duty to uphold and utilize as fully as possible in our practice these powerful moral agencies which the fathers of New England psychiatry, Todd, Woodward, Butler, and others found so efficacious in treating the insane?" (31)

V

Hospital Statistics and
Prognosis of Mental Illness

"Figures don't lie but liars can figure" is a saying which expresses an almost universal distrust of statistics. Skepticism mounts even higher when historical statistics are used to support a point of view. Data from historically remote sources can always be said to lack comparability with modern data whatever the subject matter. These difficulties become manifold when one is dealing with recovery and discharge rates from mental hospitals. Comparability of clinical material one hundred years ago and today is not easy to achieve. It is also difficult to achieve comparability between two contemporary hospitals. In neither case can we afford to ignore the quantitative data which are *available*.

Any effort to do a historical statistical study of mental illness is uniquely blessed by the fact that even the most ancient of our mental hospitals were required to submit annual reports to the state legislature. The Annual Reports of the Worcester State Hospital, beginning in 1833, contain a wealth of statistical data in an unbroken series to the present time. They provide us with a panoramic view of the traffic of patients in and out of the hospital. Fig. 3 shows what happened to the recovery rate over that period, a drop from 45% to 4%. The cry can be made that the criteria for recovery became more stringent. And indeed they did. There is also undeniable evidence that standards of treatment declined to a very low level.

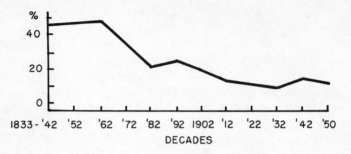

Fᴵɢ. 3. Per cent of admissions discharged as recovered from Worcester State Hospital by decades for 120 years. (*Data from the Annual Reports of the Hospital*)

The decrease in recovery rates in the post-Civil War period from the level of the early decades of the nineteenth century is by no means a new finding. Attempts to explain the decrease led to one of the most heated controversies in the history of psychiatry, namely, that concerning the curability of insanity. The pessimistic view bluntly thrust on the medical world in the 1870's by Dr. Pliny Earle's statistical studies showing lower recovery rates than those reported in the past, was followed by implications that the statistics of the earlier period had been "cooked." Since Dr. Earle wielded considerable influence and was greatly respected, other superintendents followed his lead. Among them were superintendents of the Worcester State Hospital, first Dr. Barnard Eastman and then Dr. John G. Park who followed him. Stimulated by Dr. Earle's suggestions, they compiled a retroactive report of all admissions and discharges from the day the hospital's doors were opened by Dr. Woodward. They employed their own criteria of recovery and did not distinguish between patients ill for less than one year and those ill for a longer period. The recovery rates shown in Fig. 3 were derived from Dr. Park's table covering the years from 1832 to 1892. When it is remembered that Dr. Park looked on Dr. Woodward's recovery rates with a jaundiced eye and that one of his objectives in doing the study was to demonstrate that Dr. Woodward had exaggerated his recovery rates by juggling his figures, there is little reason to suggest that the number of recoveries was exaggerated. The results of the study, however,

with respect to the years when Dr. Woodward was superintendent did not differ more than two or three per cent from
Dr. Woodward's own figures. This was never commented on
by Dr. Eastman, Dr. Park, or Dr. Earle in the Annual Reports
of the Worcester State Hospital or elsewhere. Not that they
failed to be impressed, for Dr. Park set to work on a follow-up
study (which took 10 years to complete!) of all patients discharged as recovered in the records of the Woodward regime.
It amounted to a follow-up of more than 1,000 patients over a
60-year period.

Follow-up studies of patients discharged from mental hospitals have rarely been made for a longer period than 20 years
after time of discharge. Such studies as have been made seldom
deal with more than one or two hundred patients. A follow-up
study covering a period of 36 to 60 years after discharge in-
volving over a thousand patients is therefore of considerable
interest. Evidence that these patients were discharged from the
Worcester State Hospital during the years 1833 to 1846 not
only adds to the interest, but also provides a unique opportunity
to learn about the treatment results of early American psychiatry.

The study in question was carried out between 1881 and
1892. We have inferred that the patients dealt with were discharged prior to 1847 since the total number of patients followed (1,173) is within 15 of the total number of patients
reported discharged as recovered during the years 1833-1846
(1,188). This was also the period when Dr. Woodward was
head of the hospital. In view of Dr. Pliny Earle's attack on Dr.
Woodward's reports of recovery, it is not inconceivable that Dr.
Earle suggested the follow-up study of Dr. Woodward's recovered patients in order to prove his point that the majority
relapsed. Mention of this study was first made by Dr. Park,
superintendent, in the 49th Annual Report of the Worcester
State Hospital, 1881. The following quotation from this report
discloses that his purpose was to demonstrate the unlikelihood
of recovery.

"A review of insane hospital statistics upon this subject of
recoveries, as tabulated in the annual reports of the institutions,

has brought of late to public notice the fact that a person afflicted with insanity is quite liable to a second and subsequent attacks, and that a relapse, or an attack *de novo*, occurs in this malady more frequently than in any of the other serious forms of disease.

"Now, although it may be a question upon which there may be honest differences of opinion whether each case which recovers may not be fairly called a cure, even if the patient has a second attack within a few months or a year, there can be no doubt that the public have been hitherto widely misled as to the meaning of the word 'recovery,' as used in the hospital reports, and as to the permanency of cures from insanity. Not a small number of patients who were discharged as recovered in the earlier reports of this hospital have many times since become a burden to the public or private purse by reason of a return of their malady.

"In order to obtain definite information on this point the following circular has been prepared, making inquiry about the subsequent mental condition of those patients who were discharged from this institution as recovered on their only admission, and of those who recovered on their last re-admission:

'Dear Sir,—I would esteem it a great favor if you would send me answers to the following questions (obtained either from personal knowledge or as a result of inquiry) relating to . . . . of . . . . . . , a patient discharged from this institution . . . . . .18. . . . .
Did . . . . remain well,
Has . . . . ever been in any hospital for the insane since leaving Worcester? If so, where? How many times? How long a time? and state of health after discharge.
If living, where? and mental condition. If dead, date and cause of death.
Did . . . . die at home, in hospital, or almshouse?
What was . . . .'s mental condition at time of death?
If you are unable to answer these questions, will you be kind enough to give me the address of some member of the family or acquaintance who would be likely to possess the desired information? The object of my inquiry is to perfect the medical history of the hospital.

Very respectfully,
John G. Park
Superintendent

"The above inquiries have, to this date, been made regarding only 211 patients, all of whom were discharges previous to 1840. Owing to the time which has elapsed since their connection with the hospital great difficulty has been experienced in finding anybody who knew or remembered anything about many of them. Satisfactory answers have, however, been received in 94 instances thus far, and as the cases become more recent, a much greater per cent of replies is expected." (1)

Farther on in the report Dr. Park analyzed the returns of the 94 patients about whom replies had been received. Eight were still alive and had remained well since discharge; 40 had died but had remained mentally well all their lives. Of the remaining 46, 7 had committed suicide, 10 had been re-hospitalized, and 29 were considered to be insane at the time of reply, but were not hospitalized.

In the annual report of the next year, Dr. Park revealed the full scope of the study. He also indicated that the source of motivation for doing the study lay in the person of Dr. Pliny Earle, who was at the time arousing considerable attention with his statistical studies designed to prove the incurability of mental illness.

"This subject (i.e., recoveries not permanent cures) has been elaborated at considerable length in the recent reports of Dr. Pliny Earle of the Northampton Lunatic Hospital. From information received upon this point in answer to circulars sent out inquiring about the subsequent mental condition of those persons who were discharged from this hospital as recovered on their *only admission* and of those who were discharged recovered on their *last re*-admission, it appears that of 1,171 circulars sent out, up to September 30, 1882, satisfactory answers have been received from 669. Of this number, 73 men and 80 women remained well and were living at the time of reply, and 83 men and 114 women remained well during life; 19 men and 11 women committed suicide, and the remaining 289 relapsed and had been admitted to other hospitals or had been inmates of almshouses, or had been cared for at home, where they died or are still living. No information could be obtained in 129 cases, 373 circulars remain unanswered. As was stated in my last report, a good deal of difficulty has been experienced in finding any traces of many of these cases. This is especially true of those who were committed from the cities of the state, they represent a roving population, and the records of the overseers of the poor contain no mention of them after leaving the hospital.

"I have been greatly aided by the overseers of the poor of the different towns, and by physicians and others, who have spent much time and shown much interest in obtaining for me the information furnished in table 30." (2)

In the Annual Report of 1883, Dr. Park makes the following remarks: "Information as to the subsequent history of persons who have been discharged from this hospital as recovered on their only admission or last re-admission, as tabulated in table 30, confirms the results shown in the same table last year . . . About 50 per cent suffered no relapse, but as no answers were received to one-third of the circulars sent, and taking into account the liability to relapse of those now reported well, I am inclined to believe that this percentage should be reduced one-half" (3).

This was the last mention of the follow-up study made by Dr. Park. The work of compiling statistics continued, however, until 1893 when 1,157 replies had been received of the 1,173 circulars sent out. Of the replies, 189 provided no record. Information as to the outcome of the remaining 984 patients is presented in Table 4, adapted from table 28 in the Annual Report of the Worcester State Hospital for 1893.

A total of 568 patients had either died without having a relapse or were still living and had never had a relapse. That is, very *nearly one-half (48%) never had a relapse after discharge.* An additional 67 relapsed and were hospitalized, but were again discharged (about 6%). Only 143 relapsed who were re-hospitalized (or sent to almshouses) and not again discharged. Another 142 had relapsed and were either still at home or had died while living at home.

All told, only 210 of the 1,171 patients again became a burden to the Commonwealth—less than 20%.

This unusual follow-up has remained buried in these annual reports for nearly 60 years—a sad comment on psychiatric interest

TABLE 4.—1882-1893 FOLLOW-UP OF RECOVERIES OF
1833-1846, WORCESTFR STATE HOSPITAL

Remained well, still alive	317 } (568=48%)
Remained well through life	251
Relapsed and again discharged	67
Total well or had died mentally well at 36 to 60 years follow-up point	635 = 54.13%
Relapsed, still living	100
Relapsed, died in relapse	239
Relapsed, nothing more known	10
Total mentally ill, or had died mentally ill at 36 to 60 years follow-up point	349 = 29.75%
No information	189 = 16.12%
Grand total	1,173 = 100%

(*Data from the Annual Report of the Hospital, 1893*)

in recovery from mental illness. We suggest here that the results it contained were so much better than those reported by Dr. Pliny Earle, the authority on mental health statistics of his day, that neither Dr. Park nor his successor quite dared to report those results in their full connotation for fear of arousing unfavorable comment from those who would compare them with their own results. There is no need for shyness today, however, for modern treatment results are much superior to those of the 80's and 90's of the last century. There *is* good reason to wonder, though, if a 50-year follow-up of discharged patients today would show 50% of them without relapse.

Data available today indicate that the outcome of patients treated at the Worcester State Hospital was much more favorable than Dr. Earle contended. It is therefore pertinent to review Dr. Earle's discussion of the statistical data of that hospital as presented in his book, "Curability of Insanity." The arguments he used to prove that repeated recoveries of the same patients produced falsely large recovery rates, provide a good example of his one-sided perspective. In his discussion of this matter he based his arguments on data obtained from the Annual Report of the Worcester State Hospital of 1878-79 which was written by Dr. Park.

Dr. Earle first called attention to figures which indicated that of the 47 patients discharged as recovered that year only 32 were discharged as recovered for the first time. He then made a big point of the fact that the other 15 patients had been accredited at some time in the past with a total of 55 recoveries. In making this point he disregarded his own rule that recovery figures should not be considered significant unless reported as a proportion of the number of patients admitted.

He then proceeded to analyze a special study prepared by Dr. Park of the 11,000 cases admitted to the Worcester State Hospital from its date of opening in 1833 to 1875. Dr. Earle began his analysis by pointing out that the 11,000 cases represented only 8,204 *persons,* and that the re-admissions, 2,796, amounted to one-fourth of the total number of admissions and one-third the number of persons. He then emphasized that the number of recoveries on first admissions was only 38.89% of the *persons* admitted. He also quoted the number of recoveries of all the re-admissions to be 1,191, and mentioned that the whole number of recoveries was 4,382 (3,191 plus 1,191). Here Dr. Earle called a halt to the arithmetic of recovery and failed to note that the figure for all recoveries, 4,382, was 39.1% of the total number of admissions, 11,000. He was no doubt embarrassed by the fact that this proportion is practically identical with the proportion of first admissions, or of *persons,* who recovered and were reported by him as 38.89%. Obviously he did not wish to call the reader's attention to evidence that repeated recovery of re-admissions made so little difference in the over-all recovery rate of the Worcester State Hospital. He also made no mention of the fact that the total number of recoveries of re-admissions was 1,191 of a total of 2,796 re-admissions, or 40%—which is also very close to the proportion of *persons* recovered.

After evading evidence which did not support his contentions, Dr. Earle went to the labor of calculating the per cent recovered for each successive number of admissions from 1 to 23 (which happened to be the greatest number of re-admissions reported). He tabulated the results of his calculations as follows:

1st —38.89	9th—62.92	17th —66.00
2nd—36.78	10th—62.50	18th —66.66
3rd—46.66	11th—61.11	19th —50.00
4th —45.81	12th—71.43	20th —100.00
5th —55.45	13th—66.66	21st —100.00
6th —61.29	14th—88.88	22nd—100.00
7th —61.36	15th—57.14	23rd —100.00
8th —60.60	16th—75.00	

Regarding the table he then stated: "These gradually swelling percentages are caused by the repeated recoveries of the same persons." (10). It is only too clear that Dr. Earle was going out of his way to convince the reader that repeated recoveries of the same persons caused a falsely large recovery *rate* when in fact they had no such effect. He deliberately reported percentages without giving the actual numbers of patients involved, a device which hid from the reader the information that the number of patients decreased rapidly with each successive re-admission number. Indeed, the 20th, 21st, 22nd, and 23rd re-admissions with recovery rates of 100% were all of a single patient! The data from which Dr. Earle derived his percentages appear in Table 5. Dr. Earle did not present this table because he did not want the reader to perceive that the small number of patients involved could effect the recovery rates, as recorded in annual reports, but very little one way or the other.

Dr. Earle continued his discussion by giving the number of deaths, which was 1,498, and with it the percentage of *persons* admitted which it represented, which was 18.26%. He pointed out that the proportion of deaths was nearly three times as large as was usually reported in the annual statistics of mental hospitals. Here again he sought to convince the reader that hospital reports gave more optimistic figures than was true by neglecting to note that the death rate of 18% referred to the deaths occurring in all admissions over a period of 42 years.

He then went on to quote Dr. Park to the effect that "many" patients who had swollen the number of recoveries in the past had returned to the hospital again and again and finally died there. The actual number of patients who died in the hospital on re-admission status was 318, or less than 4% of the total

TABLE 5.—Record of 11,000 Cases Admitted to
Worcester Hospital from its Opening to Sept. 28, 1875.

(*Data from a table in 1879 Annual Report of the Hospital*)

		Number of Patients				
Adm. Number	With this Number Adm.'s	Discharged			Died	In Hosp. 9-30-79
		Recov.	Improv.	Not Impr.		
1	8,204	3,191	2,218	1,524	1,180	87
2	1,683	619	471	335	224	34
3	510	238	137	63	56	6
4	227	104	74	32	13	4
5	110	61	25	13	10	1
6	62	38	15	3	6	0
7	44	27	9	3	5	0
8	33	20	10	3	0	0
9	27	17	7	2	1	0
10	24	15	8	1	0	0
11	18	11	6	1	0	0
12	14	10	2	1	1	0
13	12	8	2	1	0	1
14	9	8	1	0	0	0
15	7	4	2	0	1	0
16	4	3	1	0	0	0
17	3	2	0	1	0	0
18	3	2	0	0	1	0
19	2	1	1	0	0	0
20	1	1				
21	1	1				
22	1	1				
23	1	1				

Number of persons admitted		8,204
Number of re-admissions	2,664	
Re-admissions without removal from hospital	132	
Total number of re-admissions		2,796
Number of cases		11,000
Cases in other hospitals previous to admission here	996	
Transfers to State Hospitals in this state on 1st admission	783	
Removal to other institutions in this state on 1st admission	29	
Sent to hospitals out of state on 1st admission	15	
Transfers to State Hospitals in this state on re-admission	282	
Removal to other institutions in this state on re-admission	11	
Sent to hospitals out of state on re-admission	8	

number of persons admitted. It might also be mentioned that the number of patients re-admitted to the hospital more than twice was 461, or less than 6% of the total number admitted.

Dr. Earle's quotation of Dr. Park continued with the statement that many more patients went to other hospitals and finally died in them. It should be noted that in the follow-up study presented earlier in this chapter this was the fate of less than 6% of the number of patients discharged as recovered. A further statement of Dr. Park quoted by Dr. Earle was that still more patients had had repeated admissions and finally died in almshouses. In the follow-up study, this was the fate of less than 5% of the patients discharged as recovered.

Both Drs. Earle and Park neglect to tell what the total figure was for all patients who either had died in the hospital, were inmates of the hospital at the time of the study, or were inmates of other hospitals or almshouses. Actually it was but 2,759 (assuming that *none* of the 1,261 patients transferred to other hospitals or almshouses had been discharged), or 34%. Thus the significant finding of the entire study was left unstated, namely that 66% of the *persons* admitted had neither died in, nor were patients of, the hospital at the time of the study. He failed to mention also that 65% of the first admissions were discharged as improved and recovered. One can only surmise that Dr. Earle, and with him Dr. Park, refused to see anything in statistical data which did not support the thesis that recovery rates were artificially swollen by the repeated recovery of re-admissions.

Dr. Earle did not make explicit, but rather hid from view, his own puristic criteria of recovery which seemed to preclude the occurrence of an attack of mental illness at any time in the life of the patient. He thus mixed his concept of a recovery rate with that of a follow-up study. By this means he could always defend a pessimistic view with the argument that lifetime follow-ups would inevitably disclose many relapses of mental illness.

Whatever Dr. Earle's underlying purpose was, he succeeded in convincing the psychiatric profession that the prognosis of mental illness was extremely poor and thus exonerated its members for poor recovery rates. The idea that mental illness was incurable became more and more popular. By the turn of the century, recovery rates acceptable even to Earle (approximately 30%) seemed preposterous. By the 1920's few medical officers were inclined to discharge more than 4% or 5% as recovered. Progressive tightening of criteria for recovery and concomitant deterioration in standards of care were equally potent factors underlying this decrease in recoveries. Belief in the incurability of mental illness, which Dr. Earle had sold the medical profession, was a barrier to the adoption of much needed corrective measures which has not yet been torn down.

Not all physicians subscribed to Dr. Earle's thesis of incurability. To be sure there were few who possessed as much experience with the mentally ill as he. But among those equally experienced with Dr. Earle was Dr. Isaac Ray, the American authority on legal psychiatry, a skilled moral therapist and an enlightened hospital administrator.

Dr. Ray had demonstrated to his own satisfaction that the majority of the mentally ill were curable, in his early experience with patients during the 1840's and '50's. He was aware that much had changed in American life during the decades which followed. He could not accept Dr. Earle's devaluation of treatment results reported during the earlier decades. In 1879 he presented to the College of Physicians and Surgeons in Philadelphia a paper, "Recoveries From Mental Illness" (33), which was, in effect, a rebuttal to Dr. Earle's writings.

In this paper Dr. Ray pointed out that Dr. Earle had no basis for contending that statistical reports were more biased in favor of recovery in the early history of mental hospitals than in later years. In Dr. Ray's own view recoveries actually had become less frequent. The factors which underlay decrease in recovery in his experience were: 1) poorer general health of patients from unhygienic urban centers which were increasing in number during the course of the century, 2) the appearance of greater number of patients with cerebral affections such as general paralysis which had been all but unknown in the earlier years, 3) the more frequent hospitalization of patients with the quieter but less recoverable forms of insanity as public use of mental hospitals increased. Dr. Ray contended, furthermore, that a failure to recover was as much the result of a patient's not receiving a fair trial of (moral) treatment as the result of real incurability.

The statistical reports of the Worcester State Hospital provide us today with a working basis for estimating the prognosis of psychosis in general—at least in the earlier decades of the nineteenth century. Dr. Woodward's statistical reports show that he discharged as recovered or improved about 75% of patients ill less than one year before admission. Dr. Park's follow-up study of these recoveries shows that one-half never had a relapse.

Dr. Park's 1879 study of patients who had relapsed and were re-admitted to the Worcester State Hospital from 1833 to 1875 showed that 74% of these patients were again discharged as either recovered or improved on their last re-admission (1,961 out of 2,664). Only 12% had died during their last re-admission (318 out of 2,664).

All told, it is not unreasonable to state that, one hundred years ago, the natural history of psychosis in general (including cases due to organic changes of the central nervous system) was such that a large proportion of patients were able to leave the mental hospital, and only a small proportion, perhaps 20-30%, were destined to die in a mental hospital. Favorable outcome was, of course, even more frequent in the functional psychoses considered alone. Modern discharge rates of even 80 to 90% are of themselves not remarkable in comparison. Indeed, it is not unlikely that modern treatments merely shorten the period of illness and do not produce a greater proportion of discharges than did moral treatment.

Unfortunately there is no satisfactory scientific basis for comparing moral treatment with modern treatment, for there is no way of knowing definitely that patients admitted to mental hospitals 125 years ago were afflicted with mental disorders of the same type and severity as patients of today. It can only be said that case records of that era have many features in common with modern records, the main difference being that patients then were on the average considerably younger. Whatever the differences or similarities between two groups of patients, whether they be separated by one hundred years or one hundred miles, any claims as to their response to a particular treatment can always be challenged on the grounds that criteria for diagnosis and recovery are subjective or that selection of cases favors a particular outcome. Studies of the natural history of untreated mental illnesses are open to the same challenges.

Statistical studies of the outcome of mental illnesses which base their approach solely on the assumption that they are disease entities analogous to those of internal medicine must of necessity exclude all personal and environmental factors as mere incidentals. Thorough search and elimination of such incidentals, however, leave a remarkably small residue of cases which have objective features in common that point to the presence of the same absolute disease entity at work in all the cases. Yet because psychiatry has felt obliged to apply the scientific method, as it is known in the physical sciences, it has had no recourse but to hold to the conclusions arrived at from the study of just such a small selected minority of the patients admitted to mental hospitals: namely that the prognosis of scientifically proven psychosis is very poor and that its course cannot be altered by any known means.

It is possible to criticize the reported good results of both moral treatment and modern psychiatric treatment on the grounds that the majority of the patients treated did not have scientifically proven psychoses. By the same token it may be said that the majority of patients admitted to mental hospitals during the period of therapeutic nihilism of the latter nineteenth century were needlessly deprived of means to recovery which could have been made available to them. An alternative explanation of the low recovery rates of that particular period might be that a far greater proportion of patients had "genuine" psychosis during that period than before or since. Yet in view of the evidence that patients suffered extreme neglect during those years it does not seem a likely explanation.

From both a practical and humane point of view it is essential to learn how over-all discharge rates of mental hospitals are affected by the mode of living which patients experience. The statistics of moral treatment reported here are at least presumptive evidence that efforts to meet the personal needs of patients are well worthwhile.

VI

Moral Treatment Defined

We have suggested that moral treatment was in effect comparable to modern therapeutic efforts which include psychotherapy, occupational therapy, and recreational therapy. We have also shown that the founders of American psychiatry had an attitude of hopeful optimism with respect to the curability of insanity by means of moral treatment. We have demonstrated furthermore that their optimism was founded on a practical statistical basis. We have, then, established in some measure the value of moral treatment but have not yet shown specifically and concretely what moral treatment was.

In 1845 Pliny Earle described moral treatment at the Bloomingdale Hospital in the following words:

"In the moral regimen at this institution, every practicable effort is made to pursue that system, at once gentle, philosophical, and practical, which has resulted from the active and strenuous endeavors of many philanthropists, in the course of the last half century, to meliorate the condition of the insane. The primary object is to treat the patients, so far as their condition will possibly admit, as if they were still in the enjoyment of the healthy exercise of their mental faculties. An important desideratum for the attainment of this object is to make their condition as boarders, as comfortable as possible; that they may be the less sensible of the deprivations to which they are subjected by a removal from home. Nor is it less essential to extend them the privilege, or the right, of as much liberty, as much freedom from personal restraint as is compatible with their safety, the safety of others, and the judicious administration of other

branches of curative treatment. The courtesies of civilized and
social life are not to be forgotten, extending, as they do, to the
promotion of the first great object already mentioned, and
operating, to no inconsiderable extent, as a means of effecting
restoration to mental health." (11)

In 1847 Dr. Amariah Brigham, superintendent of the Utica
State Hospital, New York, defined moral treatment as follows:

"The removal of the insane from home and former associations, with respectful and kind treatment under all circumstances,
and in most cases manual labor, attendance on religious worship
on Sundays, the establishment of regular habits of self-control,
diversion of the mind from morbid trains of thought, are now
generally considered as essential in the moral treatment of the
Insane." (5)

The means which Dr. Earle went on to describe included
manual labor, religious worship, recreative exercise, amusements, restraints, and attendants.

In his discussion of attendants Dr. Earle made clear his
concept of moral treatment:

"It requires but little experience, in an Asylum, to convince
a person of the identity between a judicious parental government, and that system of management which is best adapted
to the insane. The motives, the influences and, as a general
rule, the means necessary for the good government of children,
are equally applicable, and equally efficient for the insane. In
fact, this system is the great desideratum, at every Asylum; and
without it, it is impossible for the management to approximate
that degree of perfection which it is desirable to attain.

"The most essential element of success in the establishment
and maintenance of such a government, is a corps of intelligent
attendants, of kind disposition, and good judgment. Such, and
such alone, can sustain a disciplinary code, founded upon kindness and supported with firmness.

"Much pains has been taken, at this institution, to procure
attendants of this character, and especially as regards the men's
department, the efforts have been rewarded with a good degree
of success. Nearly all the young men who have been so employed
during the last few years, were from the country, and so well

educated that they had been accustomed to teaching school in the winter.

"It is needless to describe, in detail, the numerous advantages of attendants of this kind over those who are ignorant, and whose only ideas of exerting control over others, are measured by the strength of their arms. He who has once tried the former, would greatly deplore the exigency which should render it necessary to return to the latter." (11)

One of Dr. Earle's favorite means of treatment was formal instruction, including lectures and school exercises:

"Soon after the writer of this article first directed his attention to the treatment of the insane, he became convinced that lectures upon scientific and miscellaneous subjects might be made an object of interest, as well as of utility, in the moral treatment of patients in public institutions. Accordingly, being at that time connected with the Frankford Asylum, near Philadelphia, he induced the managers of that institution to purchase an air pump and other philosophical apparatus, and with the aid of these he gave a series of experimental lectures before the patients, in the winter of 1841-42. The results were as favorable as had been anticipated.

"The writer became connected with the Bloomingdale Asylum in the spring of 1844, and in the autumn of the same year, encouraged by the Governors, who made a liberal appropriation for the purchase of apparatus, commenced a course of lectures, which were continued through the winter. The success was sufficient to induce perseverance in the plan, and a similar course has been delivered in each succeeding year since that time. The last commenced on October 12, 1846, and ended on May 3, 1847. It consisted of 38 lectures, as follows:

Natural Philosophy	4 Lectures
Chemistry	6
Animal Physiology	9
Astronomy	10
Physical, Intellectual, and Moral Beauty	2
Recitations of Poetry	1
History and Description of Malta	2
Greece as it was in 1838	2
Characteristics of the Americans and Europeans	2

"For the suitable illustration of the lectures, the Institution is furnished with the following apparatus:

1st — An air-pump, with its accompaniments.
2nd — A set of mechanical powers.
3rd — A magic lantern.
4th — An orrery.
5th — An electrical machine, with its implements.
6th — Pneumatic trough, receivers, retorts and other articles used in chemistry.
7th — One hundred and forty-six diagrams, painted upon bleached muslin, illustrative of the structure of the human frame, and that of the lower order of animals.
8th — Twenty similar diagrams explanatory of the laws and phenomena of light.
9th — Twenty-five astronomical diagrams.
10th — One hundred diagrams illustrating various subjects.

"The lectures were delivered in the evening and attended by an average number of about 70 patients. Their attention and deportment would compare favorably with that of the audiences ordinarily attendant upon lectures.

"It will be perceived that such subjects were selected as are susceptible of demonstration or illustration, experimentally, or through the medium of diagrams. Such topics are considered as the most suitable, inasmuch as the perceptive faculties are called into action by addressing the eye, as well as the ear. As a general rule, this holds good; but of all the lectures mentioned in the foregoing list, it is believed that none commanded more profound attention, or gave more general satisfaction, than that which consisted of the recitation of poetry, and upon the authors by whom they were written.

"As a simple method of exerting disciplinary restraint, simultaneously, over a large number of patients, a means of fixing the attention and withdrawing the minds of comparatively a multitude from the delusions incident to their disease, we believe there is no other plan, hitherto adopted in the system of moral treatment which will prove more generally and extensively useful than that of judicious and well managed lectures.

"In the autumn of 1845, a school was commenced in the men's department, and continued until the following spring. It was suspended during the winter of 1846-47. It was attended by from twenty to thirty patients, of various ages and in a diversity of conditions, in regard to mental disorder. The ordinary English branches were taught, and in these some of the younger patients made considerable progress. Others reviewed what they had previously studied, and others still, interested or amused themselves by reading from entertaining books and newspapers.

"It is not to be expected that great advancement in valuable knowledge can ever be attained in a school for the insane. The only subject generally within reach, and the only on the acquisition of which needs be expected—and this indeed is much—is the exercise of a moral control over large numbers at once; subduing excitement, rousing the inactive, and giving a new current to the thoughts.

"A miscellaneous library of about one thousand volumes is devoted to the use of the patients, and five daily and eight weekly newspapers, two monthly magazines and four quarterly reviews are also taken for them. Thus an inexhaustible fund of reading is supplied, and a librarian distributes it to such patients as are disposed to make use of it." (11)

Dr. Brigham, too, had great faith in the therapeutic value of a teaching program:

"Many cases, we believe, cannot be cured or improved, but by a rousing and calling into exercise the dormant faculties of the mind. Hence schools are beneficial, not merely to the curable class of patients, but to the demented and those approaching this condition.

"In such, the active state of the disease, which originated the mental disturbance, has passed, and left the brain and faculties of the mind in a torpid state. In these cases, medicine is generally of no use, and they cannot often be much improved, but by exercising the faculties of the mind.

"But others also benefitted by devoting a portion of every day to mental improvement. To those who are nearly or quite well, and who remain in an asylum for fear of relapsing at home, or for other reasons, schools afford enjoyment and often means for improvement which are highly valued by the patients themselves.

"The melancholy and despairing, and all those that are un-
easy and nervous, that are constantly restless and disposed to
find fault and to annoy the attendants and quarrel with all
about them, because they had nothing else to occupy their
minds, are frequently cured by mental occupation and the exercises of a school, by attending to composition, declamation, the
writing and acting of dialogues and plays.

"Various are the methods that may be adopted to awaken
into activity the dormant faculties of the mind and to dispel
delusions and melancholy trains of thought. A *museum* or collection of minerals, shells, pictures, specimens of ancient and
modern art and curiosities of all sorts, should be connected with
institutions for the insane. The opportunities are abundant for
making interesting and valuable collections of this kind by the
aid of the patients that have recovered and their friends.

"By means thus indicated institutions for the care and cure
of those affected by mental disorders will be made to resemble
those for education, rather than hospitals for the sick, or prisons
for criminals, and when we call to mind that the greater part
of those committed to such establishments are not actually sick,
and do not require medical treatment, but are suffering from
deranged intellect, feelings and passions, it is evident that a
judicious course of mental and moral discipline is most essential
for their comfort and restoration." (5)

Dr. Brigham also considered manual labor to be of therapeutic value and recommended that hospitals have a variety
of workshops available to the patients.

"Bodily labor as a measure for benefitting and curing the
insane is generally recommended and we allude to it now, but
to express the hope that better arrangements for this purpose
will be made in institutions for the insane, than have hitherto
been. Some have an insufficient quantity of land, and are destitute
of workshops. We think every such institution should have a
good farm attached to it; but still a farm is not sufficient, as it
can afford employment but to comparatively few, and only for
part of the year. We think several workshops should be connected with every large establishment for the insane, and be so
connected, that the patients of each class can go to them without

risk or exposure. One or more rooms in connection with each hall for patients, is needed in order to afford employment to all that would benefit by it. In such rooms, dress-making and tailoring, cabinet work, the manufacture of toys, basket-making, shoe-making, painting, printing, bookbinding, and various other employments may be carried on to the advantage of many patients, some of whom cannot be employed on the farm or in shops disconnected with the asylum. In the construction of asylums for the insane, we think there should be more care taken to provide convenient rooms for the purposes mentioned.

"But however useful bodily labor may be to some, we regard it as less so generally as a curative measure, and less applicable in many cases, than mental occupation or the regular and rational employment of the mind.

"In fact, manual labor, we believe, proves more beneficial by producing this result, that is, by engaging the attention and directing the mind to new subjects of thought, than by its direct effect upon the body. Not infrequently manual labor appears to be injurious, especially in recent cases; it accelerates the circulation, and sometimes reproduces excitement of mind in those who have become quiet and convalescent.

"We apprehend many have erroneous views on the subject of manual labor as a remedy for insanity. It is undoubtedly useful of itself in some cases, but it rarely cures. The large majority of patients that recover are restored without it, and most of the work performed by this class in lunatic asylums is after convalescence is well established." (5)

From the writings of Earle, Brigham, Woodward, Butler and Ray it becomes clear that moral treatment was in no sense a *single technique*. Yet it had a definable goal—that of arousing the dormant faculties of the mind. Every available means was employed to achieve this end. The very matrix of moral treatment was the communal life of patients and hospital personnel. Every aspect of daily living was utilized by the physician for its therapeutic effect in awakening feelings of companionship in the patients. The chief modalities used in awakening such feelings were those endeavors which required the patient to invest interest in something outside himself in cooperation with others, namely manual work, intellectual work, recreation, and religious worship.

Psychotherapy, as such, was not mentioned, but it took the form of patients sharing past experiences with each other and discussing these experiences both in groups and privately with their physician. Ray and Butler, in particular, emphasized the need for the physician to know the experiences of each of his patients.

Moral treatment might be defined as organized group-living in which the integration and continuity of work, play and social activities produce a meaningful total life experience in which growth of individual capacity to enjoy life has maximum opportunity.

The moral therapist acted toward his patients as though they were mentally well. He believed that kindness and forebearance were essential in dealing with them. He also believed in firmness and persistence in impressing on patients the idea that a change to more acceptable behavior was expected.

One might say that moral treatment was essentially a teaching program in how to make friends and enjoy outside interests. A hospital managed according to its principles was a going concern as productive as a university in providing individuals with greater capacity to enjoy life and take part in society. Amariah Brigham expresses this thought in the following passage: "When such a system as we have briefly indicated or rather hinted at, is judiciously introduced into asylums, with convenient rooms and suitable books and apparatus, we apprehend that trivial and objectionable amusements will be abandoned by the inmates themselves for more rational enjoyments—enjoyments which, while they serve to dispel the darkness and delusions that effect many, will at the same time have the effect to improve their minds and enable them to leave the institution not only rational, but better qualified by increased intelligence and power of selfcontrol for encountering the troubles and performing the duties of life." (5)

Moral treatment, in the *modern* technical jargon, is what we mean by resocialization through therapies with prefixes such as recreational, occupational, industrial, music—with physical education thrown in for good measure. These do not add up to moral treatment, however, either in terminology or in application. There is no equivalent to the word *moral* in use today which implies an integrated total treatment program. There is also as yet no such thing as an integrated program of social therapy in force today. And only a few hospitals are making progress in developing such a program.

The modern physician trained in dynamic psychiatry based largely on psychological concepts tends to look upon moral treatment, with its emphasis on work, play, and social activities, as being a rather naive approach to the treatment of mental illness. The most he may grant is perhaps its palliative value. He is not interested in methods not based on finding and removing the cause of illness. He cannot help but feel that the founders of American psychiatry must have been completely lacking in their understanding of mental illness to prosecute with enthusiasm such superficial measures.

It is not quite scientific, however, to judge our psychiatric forefathers as totally ignorant of the nature of mental illness simply because they did not formulate their ideas as we do today and did not use the vernacular of modern psychodynamics. We cannot assume that they were devoid of intuitive understanding of mental illness. There is ample evidence that they thought a great deal about the role of child training and psychological trauma in the causation of mental illness. They took for granted the fact that mental illness was primarily an emotional disturbance, and recognized the need to know each patient's life experience in order to be able to help him.

As therapists they were guided by the philosophical assumption of the totality of personality and were thoroughly familiar with the effect of the emotions on bodily functions. The attitude which they felt must be held toward a mentally ill patient was one which granted him the dignity of expecting him to behave in a normal way but which exercised kindness and forebearance in the face of his abnormal behavior. The inculcation of this attitude in all the hospital personnel was an important part of moral treatment.

Against the background of this attitude, coupled with the

knowledge that physicians and attendants shared the hospital living experience with the patients 24 hours a day, seven days a week, it is not difficult to see how group living could be fashioned into a highly psychotherapeutic experience.

From a psychodynamic point of view it is most significant that the superintendent of the moral treatment era often made reference to "our family" in his annual reports. The family to him included the patients and attendants as well as his own wife and children. It is not remarkable that he should feel like a father to his patients, for he ate, worked, played, and worshipped with them. It would likewise be not surprising that he should acquire a fundamental understanding of personality through prolonged and intimate contacts with his patients in a wide variety of activities and interpersonal relationships.

As we become better acquainted with the family life aspect of moral treatment we realize that, hour by hour, activities within the hospital must have contained events of great psychodynamic importance, which could be turned to therapeutic value by an experienced psychiatrist.

The forebearance of the hospital staff allowed expression of antagonism; opportunity to work at such things as carpentry, toy-making, and gardening gave release to creative urges and satisfaction for recognition. Games of chance and skill provided a setting for giving vent to competitive drives. The writing and acting of drama gave free rein to exhibitionist tendencies. The plastic arts allowed sublimation of pregenital drives. Liberty to handle sharp instruments of steel served to allay fears of impotence and mutilation. In connection with the latter, Dr. Woodward's comment in his Annual Report is of interest: "There is no employment in which they (the patients) so cheerfully engage as in haymaking. From twenty to thirty workmen were often in the field at one time, all busily employed. At one of my daily visits to the hayfield I found *four homicides* mowing together, performing their work in the best manner, and all cheerful and happy." (15)

It might be pointed out that these four homicides each did his mowing with a scythe—a tool with a three foot blade sharpened to a razor's edge.

If we reflect long enough on the attributes of moral treatment, we cannot escape concluding that moral treatment contained much that has been found of value in play therapy with children and group therapy with adults. It not only allowed freedom of expression but provided a variety of means for that expression.

We can also begin to appreciate how great the moral therapist's knowledge of a given patient's behavior must have been and how great the means he had at his command with which to modify behavior. Indeed we might even ask if psychiatrists have ever known psychotic patients so completely or labored so earnestly for their welfare. Outside the moral treatment era few psychiatrists have had opportunity for direct observation of the behavior of their patients in a variety of actual life situations. Only recently has a body of knowledge comparable in content to that of moral treatment been accumulated by workers in the interpersonal relations school of psychiatry. Their findings do not indicate that life experience in a mental hospital is of superficial importance to either patients or hospital personnel. Quite to the contrary they disclose the inadequacy of interview methods by themselves for learning how personality unfolds in the course of actual living.

Personality performance within the circumscribed situation of the interview cannot be assumed to be a representative sample of performance in the open field of society. Those who know full well the complexity of the problem involved in drawing valid conclusions from free associations produced by a patient in a single hour cannot help but feel that any attempt to draw conclusions from the vastly more complex data of social behavior is naive. Psychiatry has not yet reached the stage in which it is recognized that with the same elements there may be many orders of phenomena governed by different laws. In the field of physics, which long ago reached this stage, the researcher in the atomic structure of gases does not feel logically compelled to look upon research in meteorology as naive.

The entry of the social scientists into research in mental illness brings a still broader perspective to bear on the problem. The sociologist can investigate the role and function of a mental hospital with the same methods he would use in studying the relationship of a modern industrial company to society as a whole. The anthropologist can study mentally ill patients with the same approach he uses in studying an Indian tribe.

The absence of social science perspectives explains in part the failure of psychiatrists to apply moral treatment when charged with the care of patients whose ethnic and socio-economic background is unfamiliar to them.

VII

"Way of Life" and Mental Illness

It is the considered opinion among modern psychiatrists that mental illness is understandable as a condition in which mental traits common to all mankind are exaggerated by stressful life situations to a degree which impairs ability to get along with one's fellows. In view of this opinion it is pertinent to note the more obvious differences in the life stresses which obtained in those periods of American history when the mentally ill fared the best and the worst in the institutions created for their care.

American life in the early nineteenth century was characterized by a social structure in which the individual could experience a wide range of close human contacts. Families were large, and communities were small. There was maximum opportunity for each person to have first-hand knowledge of a large variety of personalities and behavior. The village school, town meeting house, and local church were single room structures which further accelerated getting acquainted among children and adults alike. The teacher, selectman, overseer of the poor, clergyman, and physician not only knew individuals well, but knew them as members of families and groups whose histories were known to all.

In a setting of such close enduring human relationships the needs of individuals and their sufferings at the hands of others were matters of common knowledge. Social responsibility was based on shared personal experience. Where everyone knew everyone else's affairs, interactions among individuals were strongly conditioned by a backlog of knowledge of each other which was so taken for granted that it could remain unspoken and yet be the prime factor underlying mutual understanding and determine the outcome of the interaction.

In this sort of social atmosphere the roots of personality could sink deep and radiate widely. Stability was the natural consequence of growth in the soil of highly interactive community living. Maturity and sense of responsibility came early in life. Self-support, marriage, and child-rearing began in adolescence. Professional men and artisans began their careers in their early twenties, often after serving apprenticeships to their own fathers.

Social stability, early psychosexual maturity, and respect for individuality were as much the consequence of small community life with its reservoir of common experience as of the American ideology of freedom. Indeed the small community was the proving ground of this ideology and, as such, gave it special form—the form of a society whose economic foundation was small-scale subsistence farming and handicraft.

Child-parent-grandparent relationships in this period of high birth rates were such that those past the reproductive period were in a small minority while those not yet biologically mature were in the majority. Those in the reproductive period of life occupied an intermediary position. Grandparents were not only an asset to busy farm households with many grandchildren, but were few enough to be in demand. In the absence of an educational differential between generations in the early nineteenth century, grandparents occupied a revered position as sources of wisdom and knowledge. Their reminiscences of the past were of value to their children and grandchildren since they were still pertinent to current social conditions. Times did not change rapid enough to give the recollections of grandparents a quality of irksome remoteness.

The small community era of American history was attended by stresses to which all were exposed regardless of social or economic status and which all accepted as necessary evils. Morbidity and mortality rates from infectious diseases were high, especially among infants, children, and young adults. The sorrows of sickness and death of loved ones had the effects of strengthening emotional bonds in an already intimate community life.

Richness of human contacts in early American life produced an awareness in community leaders of human needs—an awareness which led state legislatures to support the founding of public schools and state mental hospitals. Motivation underlying the creation of community services for the underprivileged was largely based on first-hand knowledge of the needs of specific individuals.

Unlike Europe, America was in the small community stage of social development when the ideas of the enlightenment became a guiding motif. The humanistic philosophies of Benjamin Franklin, Thomas Jefferson, and Tom Paine which had incubated for several decades found new impetus from men like Ralph Waldo Emerson, William Ellery Channing, Horace Mann, and Samuel Gridley Howe. The early part of the nineteenth century thus witnessed the rise to social leadership of men who were not only imbued with humanistic ideals but who also had personal knowledge of human problems from their intimate contact with small community life. The appearance of moral treatment of insanity was a natural outgrowth of the prevailing spirit of the times. The mentally ill met with the same goodwill, understanding, and sympathy that was extended to all victims of misfortune.

Moral treatment was pursued with the greatest enthusiasm and was most effective during this rather short-lived humanistic, small community phase of American history. This was a period during which mentally ill patients and their physicians both had a backlog of enduring human contacts in their life experience and shared a common cultural heritage. These factors favored understanding of patients by the physician and provided him with clues to their psychological and social needs. Physicians and patients were well versed in group living and endowed their hospitals with the qualities of genuine community life.

Moral treatment was not a specific procedure but rather a general effort to create a favorable environment in which spontaneous recovery could take place. This general effort was supplemented by a more specific effort to give whatever psychological help seemed to be needed. Recovery and discharge rates were not so much statistical representations of the result of a given treatment as they were records of the natural course of mental illnesses in general when not artificially obstructed. Moral treatment was essentially the art of eliminating obstacles and providing aids to the patient as a person. It was little more than a common sense approach to the problem of mental illness which sought, first, to learn the natural course of the illness and, second, to discover what means *already at hand* could assist the recovery process.

During the course of the nineteenth century the familiar pattern of small community life gave way to unfamiliar ever-shifting patterns of big city life in which the individual exchanged enduring contacts with relatively few people for evanescent contacts with a multitude of people. The family became smaller, more dependent on money income, and less secure. The father competed on the open market for work under employers he did not know personally. Except for his immediate family the individual was essentially alone in the midst of many. Remoteness and impersonality in human relations were increased by competition for work and wages.

These changes in the social relations of the individual took place at the same time that public leadership acquired more and more reverence for both property and materialistic science. Political and business leaders acted in accordance with "social laws" which they endowed with the validity of the law of gravitation. The legal system itself became more rigidly mechanistic. Science was not only mechanistic and materialistic but was looked upon as a body of fixed truth, hard cold facts wholly independent and outside man. Science was no longer cherished as man's brain-child or as evidence of the heights to which the human spirit could rise, as it had been in the eighteenth and early nineteenth centuries. It had become the final reality before which man must bow. Idealistic, humanistic social goals had to be abandoned in view of social laws derived from the survival-of-the-fittest version of evolution. Social leadership determined its course of action not on the basis of first-hand human experience but on the basis of reasoning from scientific premises. Impersonality in human relations, carried to the point of scientific detachment, led the educated members of society to look upon human sufferings as consequences of inexorable social laws.

Toward the end of the nineteenth century community life underwent more and more disruptions. Industry expanded immensely. Immigration increased by leaps and bounds, and more than made up for the thousands of Americans who went to take advantage of free land at the frontier. Within a few years the almshouses, hospitals, and public schools of the North Atlantic states were overcrowded with destitute immigrants. The orderly process of building a better society was interrupted. The increased flow of wealth which accompanied the exploitation of natural resources, railroad building, and expansion of factories, found its way to unexpected places. Men became rich who had once received charity. The old ideas of who was underprivileged and who was not no longer held. Many a philanthropist of earlier years found himself poorer than men he had once helped. Such disruption of relations among men left small inclination to benevolence toward mankind as a species.

One of the most vigorous proponents of the thesis that society is subject to immutable laws was William Graham Sumner, professor of Political and Social Science at Yale University from 1872 to 1909. Sumner contended: "The truth is that the social order is fixed by laws of nature precisely analogous to those of the physical order. The most that man can do is by ignorance and self-conceit to mar the operation of social laws." (12) Sumner taught that poverty belonged to the struggle for survival and objected vehemently to legislation for aid to the poor. He wrote: "A law may be passed which shall force somebody to support the hopelessly degenerate members of a society, but such a law can only perpetuate the evil and entail it on future generations with new accumulations of distress." (13) He insisted that poverty was the result of vice and derided the democratic humanitarian ideas of the eighteenth and nineteenth centuries as empty speculation. He predicted that "the mores of the twentieth century will not be tinged by humanitarianism as the last 100 years have been." (14) He urged that competition should be more vigorous and exhorted men to be frugal, sober, and wise. He specifically warned: "Let it be understood that we cannot go outside this alternative: liberty, inequality, survival of the fittest; not—liberty, equality, survival of the unfittest. The former carries society forward and favors all its best members; the latter carries society downwards and favors all its worst members." (15)

During the years that Sumner and other intellectual leaders were preaching against America's traditional democratic ideal, the middle classes were becoming more and more impersonal in their dealings with their fellow men and more careful about the company they kept. They were receptive to the sort of social attitude prescribed by Sumner, for it provided a comfortable and supposedly scientific rationale which absolved them of all guilt for any contributions they might make toward the sufferings of the less fortunate members of society.

Intolerance toward victims of misfortune which had characterized the Calvinism of colonial times reappeared in the latter part of the nineteenth century under the aegis of science. Revelation by way of sermonizing and the Bible was replaced by education as the road to power and survival. Virtue, however, was still a matter of frugality, self-denial and hard work. Its reward was still property. The old severity of Calvinism with its intolerance of the pauper as someone accused also returned. This time the work of heredity rather than the work of the devil was blamed for the pauper's blighted state. The rationalization for accepting poverty as inevitable had one advantage over Calvinism, in that it implied no responsibility whatsoever of the fit rich for the unfit poor.

Science, by the end of the nineteenth century, was no longer a means to a humanistic end. Evolutionary theory had reduced man to the status of a mere subject of physical science.

The great change in American life and thought toward the end of the last century was grimly reflected in the care given the mentally ill. Mental hospitals, as we have seen, became asylums for the hopeless.

Relationships between physicians and patients had changed greatly since the era of moral treatment. Physicians and patients, especially in the large state hospitals, no longer shared a common cultural background. Futhermore, the majority of patients came from a social class which knew no security, while the physician, become alienist, was of a class which blamed the lower stratum of society for its degraded state and prided itself on its remote and impersonal dealings with people. Mental hospitals were mere custodial institutions in which patients were given nothing more than the most meager accommodations and a diagnosis.

The attitudes of physicians toward mental illness had also undergone changes. Social distance between physician and patient, and physician and attendant fostered the development of a habit of mind which dealt with patients as cases. Lack of acquaintanceship with patients as persons and the impossibility of becoming well acquainted with many hundreds of patients were strong forces motivating physicians to seek the answers to mental illness through attempts to discover and identify physical disease entities. The very success of the methods of physical science in pathology, physiology, and bacteriology encouraged psychiatrists to adopt analogous mechanistic concepts of mental ills.

The observation by pathologists of microscopic lesions in the central nervous systems of patients who had been mentally ill made a profound impression on many psychiatrists. Mental illness, they concluded, could no longer be expected to become understandable through study of the patient's behavior. The behavior of the mentally ill could no longer be endowed with meaning having to do with the environment when it was looked upon as a result of mechanical defect in the central control station of the body.

Once the mechanical defect concept of mental illness was adopted, no such thing as true recovery could be accepted. Remissions, to be sure, might occur as in other physical disease such as multiple sclerosis, but the course of the illness could only end in death. The chief psychiatrist of mental hospitals could no longer in good faith discharge a patient as recovered. Indeed, discharge at all seemed ill-advised since relapse was considered inevitable. Also there was the chance that the patient might die at home, and the hospital lose another autopsy. From such a point of view moral treatment no longer made sense, and the cost it involved could not be justified.

The susceptibility of physicians to the dicta of the laboratory rendered them peculiarly harmful as administrators with authority over the movements of people. The mentally ill might have fared better if mental hospitals had been under the direction of lay superintendents with less respect for the findings of the laboratory science of the day.

The decline in recovery rates during the last century might have been due to an increase in the severity of mental illness itself. This does not seem likely, however, in view of the rising incidence of mental illness during the same period. The rising incidence of cancer and diabetes during the past 50 years is usually interpreted to mean that more cases are detected in their earlier and less severe forms as diagnostic ability improves. If the same reasoning be invoked to explain the rising incidence of mental illness, recovery rates should have increased rather than decreased during the nineteenth century. With mental illness, furthermore, early diagnosis was probably aided by the lesser tolerance of urban-industrial civilization for personality deviation.

The shift of psychiatry from an attitude which accepted the challenge of mental illness as a problem to be attacked with every means at hand to one which would not try anything without a guarantee from the clinical laboratory that its labors would not be in vain is a phenomenon worthy of study in itself. Psychiatry apparently did not have the courage to pursue its original course. It, too, accepted the then current notion of science that all phenomena were reducible to simple material units. Mental illness was looked upon as the result of damaged brain material.

The very idea of dead and decomposing brain cells carried with it the connotation of the patient's growing insensibility and unawareness of surroundings. The mental hospital could no longer be a citadel of hope, but had to become an asylum of despair. The psychiatrist became resigned to the task of maintaining order and cleanliness among the victims of progressive dementia. His only recommendation to the families of the

mentally ill and to society was to forget these doomed unfortu-
nates and carry on without them. To be pitied for a time and
then neglected for the remainder of life became the lot of the
mentally ill.

The significant point of interest in the history of American
psychiatry is that the highest standards of care of the mentally
ill (as gauged by present-day psychiatric criteria), obtained
when Americans lived in small communities, were inspired by
a humanistic science, and were motivated to go to the rescue
of fellow men in distress. Conversely, the lowest standards of
care obtained when Americans found themselves living in large
industrial-urban communities, were awed by the authority of
materialistic science, and were motivated to get to the top in
the competitive strife of rugged individualism. It might be said
that the Revolutionary War established the precedent of rescuing
victims of tyranny and misfortune, and that the Civil War
established the precedent of neighbor fighting neighbor for
material wealth and power. It is a moot point whether the post-
Civil War period was the more damaging to mental health.
There is no escaping the facts, however, that the incidence of
mental illness increased and that the standards of hospital care
deteriorated during that period.

It would appear that the way a society treats its mentally
ill is but a manifestation or particular instance of the way the
members of that society treat each other.

VIII

**The Development of
Scientific Psychiatry
in America**

Scientific psychiatry germinated in American mental hospitals during the last decade of the nineteenth century when the care of mentally ill had sunk to its lowest level of degradation. The plight of patients had become so shamefully distressing that even the belief that they were insensate victims of incurable brain disease could not justify the inhuman mode of life inflicted upon them. It was only after political corruption and medical incompetence reached the point of being a public scandal that progressive superintendents could gain the support necessary to introduce changes. Indeed, the medical officers of mental hospitals, as we have seen, found themselves under fire to "do something," not only by public officials, who protested that state budgets could not indefinitely stand the cost of building ever bigger institutions, but also by their medical colleagues in the specialty of neurology.

The first step toward raising the institutional care of mental patients to the standard of general hospitals was that of introducing nursing schools in mental hospitals. Many superintendents had long been disturbed on a purely humanitarian basis by the effect of ignorant, coarse, and abusive attendants on patients. They entertained the hope that young women trained in the spirit of Florence Nightingale would have a beneficial effect on the morale of patients and also aid physicians in developing a systematic clinical psychiatry. The nursing school movement began at McLean Hospital (Massachusetts) in 1885. In less than a decade, 24 more mental hospitals had opened schools of nursing.

The crucial step toward bringing psychiatry into the fold of scientific medicine was that of adding neuropathologists to the staffs of mental hospitals. This step, first taken in the 1890's, was the earliest recognition, in America at least, of the need for research in psychiatry. Neuropathologists were the physicians most thoroughly trained in the scientific method who dealt with diseases of the nervous system and were consequently the logical choice to direct psychiatric research. The first of the neuropathologists to devote his energies on a full-time basis to research in psychiatry was Dr. Adolf Meyer. His thorough-going organization of case histories, mental and physical examinations, and special laboratory studies, brought to light new findings which led to a completely new concept of mental illness. Data which had been collected to discover relationships between mental symptoms and pathological changes in brain cells or body chemistry disclosed instead an unexpected relationship between the habit-patterns of patients and their mental illness. From his study of patients' lives, Dr. Meyer concluded that mental illnesses were understandable as the particular reactions of the total personality to life stresses. On the basis of this approach, he introduced a new scientific discipline to which he gave the name of *psychobiology*.

Meyer kindled a spirit of research in American psychiatry which drew it out of its state of hopeless stagnation. His psychobiological concept of mental illness attracted workers not only in medicine but in psychology, sociology, and education as well. His prestige in medicine as a neuropathologist and his great learning outside medicine won him the position of spokesman for American psychiatry. Through him, much that was already present in American psychology was incorporated in psychiatry. The ideas of William James, John Dewey, and G. Stanley Hall, it may be noted, had already had a direct influence on at least two psychiatrists before Meyer's time. Edward Cowles, superintendent of McLean Hospital, and William Noyes, the first pathologist at McLean Hospital, both studied under Hall at

Johns Hopkins. The first issue of the American Journal of Psychology contained papers on psychiatric topics, one by Cowles on "Insistent and Fixed Ideas" and one by Noyes, "A Study of the Evolution of Systemized Delusions of Grandeur." It is also significant that Stanley Hall, although not a medical man, was for a time superintendent of a state hospital and a member of the American Psychiatric Association.

Psychological research did not long remain limited to university laboratories. The Pathological Institute of the New York State Hospitals (founded in 1896 under Van Giessen) included a psychologist on its staff, Boris Sidis, as director of research in psychopathology. Dr. Sidis (then a Ph.D. in psychology; he did not receive his M.D. until 1908) carried out research in dissociation in psychoses which demonstrated to his satisfaction that abnormal behavior used the same mechanism as normal behavior and differed only in its social pattern. This research aroused a particular interest in the psychological aspect of mental illness in two physicians, William Alanson White and Richard Henry Hutchings, both of whom later supported the psychoanalytical movement in this country. They were the first superintendents of public mental hospitals to accept psychoanalysis. They were also the first to attempt to apply principles based on scientific psychology in the care of institutionalized patients in the United States. They both received their appointments in their thirties, in the same year, 1903; Dr. White at the Government Hospital in Washington and Dr. Hutchings at the St. Lawrence Hospital in New York.

Dr. White and Dr. Hutchings brought a new optimism into mental hospital work which was reminiscent of the optimism of Dr. Todd and Dr. Woodward in the early days of moral treatment. The actual methods which White and Hutchings employed in the care of their patients were, furthermore, practically identical to those of moral treatment. They concentrated on giving attendants and nurses a psychological understanding of mental illness. They instituted occupational and recreational programs and, despite the large number of patients in their care, sought to bring individualized attention of some sort to every patient.

By the end of the first decade of this century American psychiatry was starting on its way to freedom from the deadlock of the physical disease theory of mental illness. The list of men contributing to the psychological understanding of mental illness was growing steadily. The influence of William James, Stanley Hall, and Boris Sidis had brought a number of psychiatrists and neurologists into the fold of psychology, some of whom like James J. Putnam, Isodore H. Coriat, William Alanson White, and Richard Henry Hutchings had embraced psychoanalysis. Indeed, Freud himself and Jung, too, had, through the efforts of Putnam and Hall, accepted an invitation to come to America in 1909 to express their views. Abraham Brill had begun translating Freud's writings into English in the same year.

During the first two decades of this century American psychiatry began to take on a definite form with the appointment of neuropathologists with broad background in psychology and philosophy to the directorships of mental hospitals. The earliest of these was Albert Barret at the Psychopathic Hospital at Ann Arbor, Michigan, in 1906, followed by Elmer Ernest Southard at the Boston Psychopathic Hospital in 1912, and Adolf Meyer at the Henry Phipps Psychiatric Clinic in Baltimore, in 1913.

The rapid growth of psychiatry in its psychological understanding of mental illness was accompanied by an equally rapid development in neurophysiology and biochemistry which appeared to provide new grounds for questioning the primacy of psychological interpretations. Psychiatrists and neurologists who supported the physical disease theory of mental illness thus acquired research allies. The refined histological techniques of Nissl, Alzheimer, and Ramon Y. Cajal provided new opportunities for finding brain lesions in mental illness. The biochemist provided techniques for demonstrating metabolic disorders, while researchers on the endocrine glands and autonomic nervous system opened up even greater possibilities for finding physical causes.

In New York, Dercum and Van Giessen carried out chemical studies in mental illness as early as the 1890's, and at McLean Hospital, Folin beg(an his chemical studies in 1900. The work of Hughlings Jackson, Sherrington, Brain, and Cannon in the physiology of the nervous system taken together with the findings of experimental physiological psychology seemed to provide a basis for explaining mental illness without the help of the "psychologies of past experience" as represented by Freud and Meyer.

New findings in fields of research pertinent to psychiatry, ranging from psychoanalysis to bacteriology, came in a deluge after 1900. Psychiatry which had been almost devoid of any ideas two decades before became a hot bed of new ideas and controversy. Psychiatrists in general tended to pay most attention to research results which pointed in the direction of metabolic disorders or toxins as causes of mental illness—a proclivity fostered by Emil Kraepelin's writings.

Kraepelin had a curious effect on the course of psychiatry. He brought a semblance of order out of chaos in the field of diagnosis and, at the same time, injected a note of somber pessimism into the whole matter of prognosis. He stimulated a new interest in patients' behavior at the descriptive level, for purposes of differential diagnosis. On the other hand, he succeeded in establishing mental illnesses as disease entities independent of the patient as a person, much as Thomas Sydenham had done in the field of physical ills 200 years before. Kraepelin could invoke, furthermore, all the agents of physical disease which had been discovered since Sydenham's time as causes of mental illnesses. In particular, he favored the view that the cause of dementia praecox was a disorder of metabolism.

From the time of Newton's celestial mechanics, scientists had attributed their progress in uncovering the "laws of nature" to the capacity to arrive at detached, impersonal, dehumanized "objective" abstractions. They abhorred subjective, anthropomorphic interpretations of natural phenomena as false and could not grant validity to concepts which did not have a demonstrable universal applicability. The discovery that night and day were the result of the rotation of the earth and not the rising and setting of the sun had long ago demonstrated that natural phenomena could not be explained by ordinary sense experience. In medicine, Sydenham's concept of the disease entity had proved itself to be such a useful abstraction that all progress in medicine was thought to be purely a matter of isolating more and more disease entities, observing their course, and searching for specific treatments. Kraepelin's delineation of dementia praecox and manic-depressive psychosis through painstaking descriptive studies seemed to indicate that mental ills were amenable to the same methodological approach as physical ills had proved to be. Kraepelin's views of mental ills as fixed disease entities represented a crystallization of the medical thought of the second half of the nineteenth century with respect to mental illness. As such they had a wide appeal and greatly influenced the attitudes of physicians toward mental illness, especially dementia praecox, as incurable.

Psychiatric thought at the beginning of the twentieth century was in a highly confused state of transition from the disease entity concept of mental illness to the concept of mental illnesses as reaction types. Kraepelin's concept of dementia praecox as a disease entity was largely displaced by Eugene Bleuler's concept of schizophrenia, a concept which denoted a psychological process capable of all degrees of gradation rather than a disease entity with an inevitable course. Karl Jung's studies of patients with dementia praecox demonstrated that so-called symptoms had wholly personal meaning to patients in terms of their own past experience. Psychiatry had to contend with two points of view which seemed to be mutually exclusive. Mental illness was either a universal disease entity or a unique reaction to life experience in each patient. Progress toward resolution of these two points of view came with the development of a broader perspective which took greater account of the similarity of personal experiences, feelings, and thoughts among mankind in general as well as among the mentally ill of the world. The very universality of certain behavior patterns which had been the basis for designating a disease entity turned out to be understandable as an example of the universality of supposedly unique and personal inner-life experiences. The concept that psychic experiences could in any sense approach being both personal and universal was a contribution to modern thought which was formulated in a general way by Adolf Meyer, and in a specific and more revolutionary way by Sigmund Freud.

During the first two decades of the present century, psychiatry increased its scope from that of a purely medical discipline to one which included the study of psychological and social factors in mental illness. This trend is well represented in the writings of Elmer E. Southard. From 1901 to 1910, he wrote on histopathology and physical disease entities only. From 1911 to 1920, his writings included many papers on the psychological and sociological aspects of mental illness. One of his chief contributions during the latter decade, while he was director of the Boston Psychopathic Hospital, was the development of the concept of social psychiatry and the founding of psychiatric social work.

Meyer's psychobiology, Freud's psychoanalysis, and Southard's social psychiatry strongly implied or explicity pointed to the role of other people in both the pathogenesis and healing of mental illness. This concept, in some measure, owed its acceptance to a recovered patient by the name of Clifford Beers who told the world of the experiences in mental hospitals which had retarded his recovery. The timing of his story was such that it dovetailed with the concepts emerging in psychiatry, and at the same time caught the public in a receptive mood. His book, "A Mind that Found Itself," published in 1908, was directly instrumental in leading to the founding of the National Committee for Mental Hygiene which chose Beers as its Secretary.

The importance of psychological and social factors in the genesis and recovery of mental illness was largely accepted by leaders in American psychiatry before the first World War. When the United States entered the war, organized American psychiatry was prepared to take psychological factors into account in the care of mental disorders of soldiers. The director of the National Committee for Mental Hygiene, Dr. Thomas Salmon, was appointed chief psychiatrist of the expeditionary forces to Europe. From his experience with war conversion hysteria among soldiers in France, he described (20) the emotional conflict underlying that disorder as the result of "the many demands of the instinct of self preservation stirring deep and strong affective currents against the conscious expectations, desires and requirements of 'soldierly ideals,' imbedded in a matrix of discipline."

French neurologists expressed similar views, placing emphasis on outside stresses rather than on individual susceptibility. Babinski stated in his book (with Froment) on hysteria in the first World War: "The hysterical symptoms observed at the present time . . . appear to develop chiefly as the result of moral and physical strain, and of commotions which demand the physical resistance of the individual and predispose him to nervous disorders of this kind, however unsusceptible he may appear . . . It is undoubtedly one of the most widespread affections and for my part I am inclined to believe that there are very few individuals who escape when placed in certain circumstances, and under the influence of more or less active occasional causes." (4)

The British psychiatrist, Dr. Frederick Mott, demonstrated the psychological character of a great majority of so-called shell shock cases and emphasized the importance of moral and hospital atmosphere in the treatment of war neuroses in general. Another war experience was the breakdown of soldiers with symptoms of dementia praecox who recovered on return to the United States.

The theoretical structure of psychoanalysis was also changed by the war. Freud no longer considered the erotic drives to be the only source of motivation but included aggressive drives as a determining factor in personality development. After the war, Freud's studies of transference and Harry Stack Sullivan's elaboration of his concept of psychiatry as the science of interpersonal relations brought psychiatry another step closer to the social sciences. Another development after the first World War was the founding of a psychoanalytic sanatarium in a suburb of Berlin, under the direction of Dr. Ernst Simmel. The problem of 24-hour care of patients was one hitherto not encountered by psychoanalysts. It became immediately apparent that the course of a patient's illness was in considerable measure dependent upon relationships with other patients, attendants, and nurses as well as on his relationship to his analyst during the interview hour. In 1937, a psychoanalytic sanatarium began operation in the United States—the Menninger Clinic in Topeka, Kansas. The experience of this clinic highlighted the need for research to learn what sort of social environment was thera-peutic. This led to an attempt to prescribe the kind of attitude personnel should have toward each patient, known as "attitude therapy." The concept of "milieu therapy" also appeared.

In 1938, the first papers appeared reporting social research of interaction processes in mental hospital wards (34). Since that time, an increasing amount of such research has been done.

Psychiatric progress from the time Meyer began his work was largely in the form of increased knowledge of the role of psychological factors in mental illness and in histologic studies, showing the absence of organic brain changes in so-called func-tional psychoses. Research in metabolism, endocrinology, and neurophysiology, however, was going ahead during the same years but with results of little immediate importance to psychia-try.

The contribution of neurophysiology to psychiatry has its origin with Hughlings Jackson's work, showing the hierarchical organization of the central nervous system and Sherrington's work, showing the inhibitory action of higher centers on lower. This work was followed by John F. Fulton's research on the frontal lobes of chimpanzees. Sections of the frontal lobes lead to more tranquil behavior, a result which led the Portuguese physician, Egaz Moniz, to try lobotomy on chronic psychotic patients, a venture which had promising results. Another area of physiological research of importance to psychiatry was that of Walter B. Cannon, showing the relationship of the autonomic nervous system to epinephrine, a finding which was followed by further studies showing the disrupting effect of fear states and of epinephrine on adaptive behavior. This latter finding led to Manfred Sakel's theory that in schizophrenia an epineph-rine-like substance is impairing cellular function of the cerebral cortex, a theory which led him to give insulin (the "antagonist of epinephrine") to schizophrenic patients. The surprisingly good recovery rates achieved by this treatment led to its wide-spread adoption after the middle 1930's. Shortly thereafter, Meduna theorized that schizophrenia and epilepsy were antagon-istic conditions and attempted to treat schizophrenic patients with convulsion-inducing doses of metrazol. This method also achieved good results. Shortly thereafter, Cerletti and Bini used electric shock to induce convulsions and obtained similar results. This treatment was then tried in manic-depressive psychosis and found to be even more effective in that condition. Thus research in physiology led to many "hunches" in treatment which were effective and contributed further to psychiatric progress.

Research in psychology and psychopathology has shown that mental illness in an individual cannot be understood without taking into account his interactions with his family and with society. Research in physiology and psychosomatic medicine, on the other hand, has demonstrated the effect of emotions on body functions, while new knowledge of endocrine secretions has provided a rationale relating body chemistry to body build (Kretchmer). The picture of mental illness which is emerging from research in the now strongly related fields of psychiatry, physiology, and sociology is one in which a circular series of events occur, beginning with social factors which produce psychological changes. These psychological changes then, depending on the individual's constitutional inheritance, alter physiological function which is accompanied by further psychological changes. Change in behavior elicits further reactions from society which once again produce psychological changes in the individual and repeat the cycle.

With progress of research, it is becoming increasingly clear that the treatment of mental illness involves the development of techniques for interrupting this cycle at one or the other or all of these levels. In some forms of mental illness, judicious change in the social environment alone will arrest the disease process; in others individual psychotherapy or group psychotherapy may be needed in addition. More severe forms of illness may require electric shock, insulin coma, or even psychosurgery.

The rapidly growing knowledge of the profound effects of personalities on each other is the most challenging aspect of modern psychiatry. Hospital atmosphere, morale, *esprit de corps* and motivation of all personnel who contact patients are matters of immense importance. Of even greater importance is the need for perceptiveness and intelligent understanding of patients by all who come in contact with them. A modern mental hospital, to perform its functions, must be a perennial enterprise in social engineering and education. Consequently, administrative psychiatry assumes a new importance in the treatment of mental illness. It is a little humiliating to realize that modern psychiatry is fast approaching a point of view similar to that of moral treatment as it was practiced by the founders of the American Psychiatric Association well over one hundred years ago. Though our knowledge of mental illness today is more precise and more explicit in many areas, it is doubtful that our philosophical background or human understanding is significantly greater.

The great gains made in psychiatric knowledge in the past fifty years would be valid grounds for hope and optimism were it not for the discouraging fact that only a small minority of mentally ill patients in America benefit from the knowledge gained. Indeed, conditions in mental hospitals are so unacceptable that they were referred to, as recently as 1948, as the "Shame of the States." (8)

To understand why the majority of American mental hospitals are not providing the standard of treatment achieved by a small minority would require a large scale sociological study.

The modern concept that mental illness is a reaction to past and present relationships with other people is understandably repugnant to our society, since such a view implies that our society itself is the ultimate cause. It means that we actually do "drive" our close associates insane—something we admit only in jest. Furthermore, modern concepts of treatment which hold that mental illness is curable through relationships with other people place the responsibility to provide such relationships squarely upon our shoulders. We become even more uncomfortable when faced with the proposition that sanity and insanity are not a matter of black and white, but a relative affair depending on the adjustment of individuals to each other. Such a proposition raises the question of our own mental health. Indeed, the whole issue of mental illness becomes so unsavory at this point that we would rather put it out of mind altogether.

We have pretty much succeeded in keeping mental illness out of sight and out of mind for several generations. Medicine and law have rendered committed patients almost impotent to obtain a hearing in their own behalf. In spite of their relative helplessness they have made themselves felt, for by their very increase in numbers and failure to recover they have come to cost our society more than we like to pay for their keep. The time is at hand when we cannot afford to continue managing their lives as if they all had hopeless structural brain defects. We have long enough permitted ourselves the luxury of isolating the mentally ill to spare ourselves the shock of seeing in them our own unacceptable traits and motives. We have long enough blinded ourselves to their great sensitivity and need for companionship with the rationalization that they were "too far gone" and insensible of their surroundings to benefit from anything we could do.

Mental hospitals which have investigated the modes of dealing with patients among hospital personnel have learned that the course of mental illness is intimately related to the relative availability of means which meet the minute by minute psychological needs of individual patients. Whereas interpretation of the patient's behavior has been the emphasis of modern dynamic psychiatry, research in the social psychiatry of hospital wards is showing the importance of the patient's interpretation of the behavior of those who control him. This brings to the fore the necessity that those who attend the mentally ill understand their own behavior in order to avoid obstructing the recovery of patients. The humility required of mental hospital personnel to achieve knowledge of self is a serious demand paralleling that placed on individuals who dedicate their lives to religious or military service.

The keen perceptivity to human needs which mental hospital personnel must achieve in order to do justice to patients presents a challenge to our entire society; for it indicates how little human needs are met in other institutions, including families, schools, offices, and factories—from where patients come. Psychiatry has the responsibility of informing the public of the needs of the mentally ill. Psychiatry also has the function of training those members of society who are motivated to work toward the recovery of patients. The community has the ultimate responsibility of seeing to it that the means are provided for *applying psychia-*

tric knowledge. Mental illness to a greater extent than any other is, from inception to cure, *primarily* a social problem.

It is over 50 years since modern scientific psychiatry recognized the importance of total life experience in the etiology of mental illness. It is only recently that psychiatry has begun to appreciate the significance of *total life experience in the treatment of mental illness,* and to understand how impersonal custodial care en masse only prolongs, or produces another kind of, mental illness.

IX

The Problem of
Treatment in the
Traditional Mental Hospital

The history of institutional care of the mentally ill may be separated into three phases: 1) the moral treatment phase, 2) the custodial non-treatment phase, and 3) the custodial re-education phase. Today we are on the threshold of a fourth phase, namely that of therapeutic research.

Modern therapeutic research in psychiatry embraces three scientific disciplines: the physiological, the psychological, and the sociological. As such it presents the first opportunity in the history of medicine for the development of an integrated approach to the scientific treatment of mental illness.

The inclusion of social science theory and methodology in psychiatric research introduces a new basis not only for evaluating the needs of patients but also for evaluating psychiatric theory and practice. It is particularly pertinent to the study of institutional psychiatry, for it provides a frame of reference for identifying habitually unrecognized and unquestioned values and attitudes, and for determining their effects on the social adjustment of patients.

Viewed from the perspectives of social science, the history of institutional psychiatry becomes intelligible in terms of the social and psychological effects of medical concepts of mental illness, regardless of their scientific validity. From this point of view the significant aspect of the earliest phase of institutional psychiatry, that of moral treatment, is that it had its origin in the pre-scientific era of medicine and drew its inspiration from the same philosophy of human equality and individual rights that gave rise to our democratic political institutions. It belonged more to the humanitarian liberal movement than to medical science. As such it paid full attention to patients as persons.

The custodial non-treatment phase of institutional care was concurrent with the early phase of scientific medicine and was conditioned by the impersonal outlook of an emergent technological industrial society. The authoritative scientific verdict that mental illness was due to incurable brain disease eliminated the belief, on which moral treatment was based, that patients were capable of responding as persons to sympathetic human understanding. Since no scientific treatment for mental illness had yet been discovered, mental hospitals became mere receptacles for the incurable.

The re-educational phase of custodial care represented a more hopeful positive attitude toward patients in that they were regarded as teachable. Occupational and industrial therapies were formally recognized and introduced as treatment measures. Acceptance of the idea of re-education or training as treatment did not, however, indicate a change in the medical attitude that the lesions of mental disease were incurable. At most it amounted to a concession that patients could be taught to behave *like* rational human beings.

Adoption of the view that the goal of the mental hospital was to train patients to do useful work placed patients in a new relationship to the hospital. Since all the training they received was in those occupations necessary to the operation of the hospital, the patients found themselves to be participants in the business of keeping the hospital going. The fact that the greater proportion of the actual work done in mental hospitals came to be done by patients demonstrated the economic success of the training endeavor. The patients benefited from the measure of self-respect they gained from being contributing members to the hospital society. Regardless of how well they did their work, however, professional concepts of their mental condition prevented their being fully accepted as co-workers or as persons.

Professional belief in the permanence of the lesions of mental disease was attended by a reluctance to release patients from the hospital even though they performed the same duties as normal rational people. The resulting accumulation of patients inevitably led to a large pool of unemployed and hence unfavored patients. These patients constituted a social class which ranked at the bottom of the hospital caste system.

The concept that mentally ill patients were incurable but teachable accelerated the development of the mental hospital into an authoritarian stratified class society, governed by the principle of punishment and reward in pursuing its goal of controlling and training the lower classes. The living conditions of the lower classes were characterized by austerity, deprivation, and bleakness. Such living conditions were entirely consistent with the value judgment that patients were less worthy and less able to appreciate the better things of life than the upper classes.

This value judgment was, in fact, reflected in *all* relations between hospital personnel and patients. The sheer multitude of patients as compared with the personnel was in itself a contributing cause to remote impersonal attitudes toward patients. Belief that patients were intrinsically irrational and unpredictable completely undermined any spontaneous inclinations on the part of personnel to treat patients as persons in their own right. The attitudes of personnel, derived from such belief, indicated to the patient that he lacked some essential human quality, and that his only hope for approval lay in obeying orders and deporting himself as an impersonal, unquestioning individual.

The system of mental hospital management, in the course of its development, has adopted many of the practices of business, industry, and scientific agriculture. Today the mental hospital with its farms, truck gardens, shops, and power plants is a complete community operating at a high level of efficiency. In some respects it is typical of many large American enterprises and takes pride in its bigness. But from the standpoint of modern psychiatry and sociology it is anachronistic and unproductive, for it neither gives patients the benefit of the best treatments known to psychiatric science nor employees the benefits of modern democratic principles of industrial organization. From the perspective of modern history, furthermore, the mental hospital stands almost alone as an example of an institution which invests its energies in preserving customs and traditions rather than in making progressive innovations.

Absence of the treatment motif in mental hospitals places all professional personnel in a contradictory role, but it is the attendant who occupies the most difficult and frustrating position. He serves as guard and taskmaster whose duty it is to preserve order by restricting patients' spontaneous movements to a minimum and by closely supervising any duty he directs the patient to perform. He is the most important person in the patient's life, but his position in the hospital hierarchy is of the lowest order. He is subjected to a rigid discipline which requires him to maintain an impersonal relationship with patients and holds him responsible for any mishap which occurs. He must constantly be on the lookout lest some patient acquire a bit of glass, a length of rope, a sliver of wood, or a supply of matches; for every patient is suspect of harboring violent tendencies or desires to escape. He must even restrict conversation between patients lest altercations result. He is fulfilling his duties well if he is observed to be presiding over a scene of somber silence when the supervisor, nurse, or physician "trips" through his ward. All told, his task is a thankless one, for like the patient he remains in good standing only so long as there are no mishaps. There is no way he can progress or better himself. At best, his prospect is the monotony of uneventful life on a "well-managed" ward. His very acceptance of low pay bespeaks in his own mind and in the mind of others that his work is little respected. And in the public mind his capacity to endure close association with the fancied depravity of the mentally ill places him in a category as uniquely stigmatized as mental illness itself.

In order to preserve self-esteem the attendant explains his work in a way which implies admirable qualities of some sort in himself. He emphasizes to others the hazards of his job and pictures in detail the savage cunning or impulsive violence of his patients. He thereby attributes to himself the socially valued qualities of shrewdness and courage, and casts himself in the role of protector of society against madmen. In order to keep intact this version of his role, he must conceive his relationship to patients to be that of perpetual warfare or at best an armed truce. His chief weapons in this warfare come to be a severe countenance and a forbidding manner betokening mastery over the patients. The sounds of enraged pounding and loud cursing emanating form the seclusion rooms are convincing evidence to patients of the futility of anything more than passive resistance.

The connotation that an attendant's friendship with a patient is a reflection on his own mental health is a force which preserves the ever-present barrier between patients and attendants. Indeed, the attendant who does become friendly with patients not only runs the risk of being an outcast among his fellow attendants but also risks reprimand by the ward physician. The capacity of a patient to form friendships with hospital personnel represents a threat to the impersonal authority of the hospital. Anyone less well trained than the physician is automatically considered susceptible of being "taken in" by a patient's efforts to demonstrate his sanity and the injustice of his incarceration. On the other hand, the long-standing distrust of the attendant's character raises in the physician's mind the question of the harmful effect on the vulnerable patient of anything more than an impersonal relationship with attendants. To the extent that this bias is in any measure justifiable, it is a consequence of the hospital's own policy of selecting for attendants individuals who are forced by circumstances to work for low pay in the degrading environment of ward life.

This policy reflects the attitude that neither the mentally ill nor those who will accept work close to them are to be trusted. Indeed, the attendant charged with preventing violence is under constant suspicion of using force and violence himself. He is furthermore subjected to the control of the professional registered nurse and placed under restrictions which often vary only in degree from those inflicted on patients. In some hospitals the male attendant is not even permitted to associate with nurses or other female personnel, such as office workers who "outrank" him. His position, except in his relation to patients, is largely that of a flunky who may be summarily discharged for not "knowing his place."

The nurse in the mental hospital has, except in the infirmary, little to do with the patient as a sick person. Her chief function is that of providing more complete medical control and authoritarian discipline throughout the hospital than physicians can achieve unassisted. The physician as a healer of the mentally sick, also has nothing to do with the patient. He performs the function of guardianship over the patient's physical health and safety.

The mental hospital's relationship with its patients is entirely predicated on the thesis that the patient cannot be trusted and must therefore be kept under complete control. Indeed the very essence of the function of the mental hospital is that of controlling and protecting. The attendant controls the patients and protects them from each other. The nurse controls the attendant and protects the patient against his harshness or laxity. The physician controls the nurse and protects her against supposedly unprincipled attendants, while the superintendent controls his physicians and protects them against the critical public.

The energies of the hospital staff are expended in maintaining personnel at a high pitch of alertness to all signs of impending violence of patients. The prevailing psychological climate is one resembling military vigilance against attack. High value is placed on unquestioning obedience to authority, and traditional hospital customs and procedures are revered for their ostensibly time-proven worth in averting disaster. Proposed changes are viewed as threats to the security of all concerned. The entire hospital society has a vested interest in the status quo and looks to the superintendent as the greatest single stabilizing force assuring its preservation.

The modern psychiatrist who assumes the role of superintendent of a traditional mental hospital and makes plans for giving his patients the benefits of a full psychiatric treatment program thus finds himself confronted with the problem of how to change the structure, the function, and the attitudes and values of a deeply rooted social system. He cannot leave it unchanged and attain the quality of interpersonal relation and social atmosphere essential to psychiatric treatment.

He is faced with the immediate and vital necessity of firmly establishing, in the minds of all, his own and the hospital's attitude of respect for patients—by raising the standard of their living accomodations to the level which is customarily expected by self-respecting citizens; by securing facilities for vocational training, education, recreation, and entertainment which are on a par with those available to the general public; by sparing patients the indignity of indiscriminate detention behind locked doors; by recognizing the right of patients to participate in their own government and in the administrative affairs of the hospital. Once these steps have been taken, the superintendent can proceed in his plans for imparting to all personnel a wholly new philosophy of mental illness and an understanding in its treatment.

Yet even these necessary and elemental steps cannot be taken without a large increase in the funds made available to the hospital. At present the average public mental hospital must hold its *weekly* operating expenses per patient to a figure less than the *daily* operating expenses of the average general hospital. Such a small budget forces the superintendent to improvise, and offers little prospect of doing more than raise hopes which end in frustration and discouragement. A possible alternative is that of diverting funds from the care of chronic cases and applying them to a treatment program for acute cases. This alternative could be supported on the grounds that no program of treatment has yet been developed for chronic cases comparable to that known to be effective with acute cases. It has, however, the unpalatable aspect of depriving the many for the benefit of the few—an aspect which could be obviated by research in experimental development of life experience treatment programs for chronic cases.

Another major obstacle to the establishment of full treatment programs in mental hospitals is the shortage of trained professional psychiatric workers. Solution of this problem at the level of the mental hospital calls for research in methods of educating non-professional personnel in the psychiatric care of patients.

Modern psychiatry, as it has been developed in the teaching centers of the world, encompasses so many scientific disciplines that it is beyond the capacity of any one man to master all of it. This raises the question of whether the traditional hierarchical organization of the mental hospital does not have disadvantages which impede its growth as a scientific institution. The superintendent is legally charged with full responsibility for every patient committted to his hospital. He is not free to delegate this responsibility to his staff; he can only delegate authority to act. This state of affairs favors reliance on routine and established precedent; it prejudices against acceptance of new concepts and procedures. There is, however, as yet no basis from experience for concluding that a different form of organization would be more conducive to psychiatric advancement. The example of the general hospital suggests that greater advances are made when professionally independent physicians work together as members of autonomous and competitive medical services and are served by a superintendent whose chief role is that of providing them the means for achieving their goals.

In his over-all endeavor to bring modern treatments into the traditional mental hospital the superintendent is impeded not only by deeply rooted attitudes within the hospital but also by equally fixed attitudes in the general public. Public attitudes toward the institutionalized mentally ill lag far behind advances in psychiatric thought. They are an echo of psychiatric attitudes, current 50 years ago, when "insanity" was considered to be an untreatable disease of the brain. To the public mind, mental illness does not carry the connotation of an illness which anyone may have; it designates rather a class of human beings membership in which differentiates an individual as immutably as does race membership. The public mind also characterizes the mentally ill patient as being so completely untrustworthy, unpredictable, and dangerous and indecent that he must be kept under control at all times. These misconceptions of mental illness are serious enough because of the unjust and false stigma which they place upon a large number of our citizens; but of greater importance is that the traditional mental hospital of today operates in accordance with these same misconceptions.

The superintendent who would make modern psychiatric treatment available to his patients must recognize that the community cannot reasonably be expected to change in attitudes or alter its social or financial relations with the hospital on demand. His position is analogous to that of the modern medical emissary to a primitive land who must demonstrate to the people the advantages of modern medicine over primitive medicine before he can win their support in founding a modern medical clinic. The superintendent of the mental hospital must go a step beyond this, for his treatment of patients is not limited to technical matters which need not be understood by the community. On the contrary, he deals with problems which cannot be solved without community understanding and participation. His professional function is not limited to treatment of patients in the hospital but includes treatment of the attitudes of the larger community of which the hospital is a part. These problems of community dread of the hospital, misconceptions about its patients, and the general poverty of the hospital are also due to the pathologic conditions which require research and development of therapeutic skill.

The superintendent's success in securing treatment for his patients hangs largely on his success in establishing multiple points of close and enduring contact between the mental hospital and the community. The more intimately acquainted socially active members of the community become with patients, the more opportunity they will have to acquire an appreciation that the mentally ill are people in painfully difficult situations of a complexity that would defy anyone's capacity for explanation and impair anyone's ability to get along in a society blind to the complexities of human relations. Such appreciation can win patients the respect and consideration which are their due both as sick people and as members of our society.

Growth of understanding in the community that mental illness has to do with the frustrations, disappointments, and injured sentiments which people unwittingly inflict on each other can lead to recognition that sub-standard living conditions and imprisonment only add injury to the patient's already damaged self-esteem. From acquaintanceship with recovered patients can come a general realization in the community that mental illness is not incurable but that its cure requires far more of human thought and effort in behalf of patients than is now given.

The policy of inviting the community to participate in the daily life of the mental hospital allows the public an opportunity to discover that their "good Samaritanism" does not go unrewarded. Visitors can learn that patients in their efforts to get well have done a great deal of creative thinking about human relations and can teach others much that will help them in their own life situations. This positive aspect of the mental hospital provides a basis for its development as an educational center of great value to the community. Indeed, it is not an extravagant speculation that mental hospitals will be a nucleus of future progress in man's understanding of man, for they are natural centers for study and research in human relations.

One lesson which can be derived from the history of institutional care of the mentally ill is that human beings are molded by whatever authority they respect, and that ideas about human beings of authoritative origin eventually influence human behavior in a direction which confirms the authoritative idea.

Psychiatry as a member of the science family enjoys immense prestige as the final authority on illness of the human mind. People with sick minds, moreover, are highly sensitive to the opinions and attitudes of other people. They are profoundly affected by the fact that the law of the land has committed them to the care and custody of the mental hospital and are even more profoundly affected by the hospital's opinion of them. The history of institutional care demonstrates the different effects of optimism and pessimism. Recovery was far more frequent during the optimistic era of moral treatment than it has been since the advent of the pessimistic era of custodial care.

Modern psychiatry, founded on psychology and the social sciences as well as physiology, is alert to the role played by attitudes and interpersonal relations in determining the course of mental illness. Research studies in social therapy have led to the adoption of treatment programs which have greatly increased the frequency of recovery. At present such programs of treatment are to be found in only a few teaching hospitals. Over 99% of the mentally ill in America receive nothing more than custodial care of low standard. The real problem of mental illness today is that of motivating our society to re-instate the human rights of this great number of patients and to provide them with psychiatric treatments which have already proven their worth.

Respect for the feelings of mentally ill patients has already begun to increase scientific sensitivity to the psychic pain and emotional suffering which underlies distorted thinking and behavior. Search for chemical means for allaying such pain and suffering has established the new field of research called psychopharmacology.

The fact that this research has resulted in the discovery of drugs which have contributed greatly to the well-being of thousands of patients over the past decade is convincing evidence that serious attention to the simple human needs of the mentally ill should be a matter of great concern to everyone.

Bibliography

1. Annual Report of the Worcester State Hospital, 1881.
2. Annual Report of the Worcester State Hospital, 1882.
3. Annual Report of the Worcester State Hospital, 1883.
4. Babinski, J., and Froment, J.: *Hysteria or Pithiatism*. London: London University Press, Ltd., 1918, pp. 28-29.
5. Brigham, A.: Moral treatment. *Am. J. Insanity, 4*: 1-15, 1847.
6. Bucknill, J. C., and Tuke, D. H.: *A Manual of Psychological Medicine*. London: John Churchill, 1858, p. 9.
7. Butler, J. S.: *Curability of Insanity* and *The Individualized Treatment of the Insane*. New York: G. P. Putnam's Sons, 1887.
8. Deutsch, A.: *Shame of the States*. New York: Harcourt Brace and Company, 1948.
9. Dickens, C.: *American Notes*. Leipzig: Bernard Tauchnitz, 1842.
10. Earle, P.: *Curability of Insanity*. Philadelphia: J. B. Lippincott Company, 1887.
11. Earle, P.: *History, Description and Statistics of the Bloomingdale Asylum of the Insane*. New York: Egberg, Hovey and King, Printers, 1849.
12. *Essays of William Graham Sumner*, Vol II. New Haven: Yale University Press, 1934, p. 107.
13. *Ibid.*: p. 100.
14. *Ibid.*: Vol. I, pp. 86-87.
15. *Ibid.*: Vol. II, p. 95.
16. First Annual Report of Worcester State Hospital, 1833.
17. Gray, J. P.: Insanity: Its frequency: and some of its preventable causes. *Am. J. Insanity, 42*: 1-45, 1885-1886.
18. *Ibid.*: p. 277.
19. *Ibid.*: p. 278.
20. Hall, J. H., Zilboorg, G., and Bunker, H. A.: *One Hundred Years of American Psychiatry*. New York: Columbia University Press, 1944, p. 386.
21. Hammond, W. A.: The non-asylum treatment of the insane. Trans. M. Soc., N.Y., Syracuse, 1879.
22. James, W.: Letter to Clifford Beers. In *A Mind That Found Itself*. New York: Doubleday, Doran and Company, Inc., 1939, p. 261.

23. Kelly, H. A., and Burrage, W. L.: *American Medical Biographies.* Baltimore: The Norman, Remington Company, 1920.

24. Mitchell, S. W.: *Address before the Fifteenth Annual Meeting of the American Medico-Psychological Association.* Trans. Am. Medico-Psychol. A., Vol. I, 1894.

25. Page, C. W.: Dr. Eli Todd and the Hartford Retreat. *Am. J. Insanity, 69:* 761-785, 1912-1913, p. 783.

26. *Ibid.:* p. 663.

27. *Ibid.:* p. 782.

28. *Ibid.:* p. 779.

29. Page, C. W., and Butler, J. S.: The man and his hospital methods. *Am. J. Insanity, 57:* 477-499, 1901, p. 490.

30. *Ibid.:* p. 481.

31. *Ibid.:* p. 499.

32. Pinel, P.: *A Treatise on Insanity.* Translated from the French by D. D. Davis, M.D., 1806.

33. Ray, I.: Recoveries from mental illness. *M. & Surg. Reporter, 41:* 72-74, 1879.

34. Rowland, H.: Interaction processes in the state mental hospital. *Psychiatry, 1:* 323-337, 1938.

35. Sanborn, F. B.: *Memoirs of Pliny Earle, M.D.* Boston: Damrell and Upham, 1898, p. 306.

36. *Ibid.:* p. 306.

37. *Ibid.:* p. 150.

38. *Ibid.:* p. 263.

39. *Ibid.:* p. 362.

40. *Ibid.:* p. 281.

41. *Ibid.:* p. 151.

42. *Ibid.:* p. 274.

43. *Ibid.:* p. 299.

44. Williams, S. W.: *American Medical Biography,* Greenfield, Mass.: S. Merriam and Company, Printers, 1845.

45. Woodward, S. B.: Annual Report of the Worcester Lunatic Hospital, 1842.